GRAMMAR
Form and Function

2A

Workbook

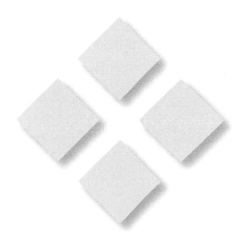

Milada Broukal
Amy Parker

McGraw-Hill

Grammar Form and Function 2A

 This book is printed on recycled, acid-free paper containing 10% postconsumer waste.

3 4 5 6 7 8 9 QPD 9 8 7 6 5

ISBN: 0-07-301379-X

Editorial director: Tina B. Carver
Executive editor: Erik Gundersen
Senior developmental editor: Annie Sullivan
Editorial assistant: Kasey Williamson
Production manager: MaryRose Malley
Cover design: Preface, Inc.
Interior design: Preface, Inc.
Art: Eldon Doty, Preface, Inc.

Photo credits:
All photos are courtesy of Getty Images Royalty-Free Collection.

The *McGraw-Hill* Companies

Contents

UNIT 3 THE FUTURE TENSES

UNIT 4 NOUNS, ARTICLES, AND QUANTITY

UNIT 5   PRONOUNS

UNIT 6   THE PERFECT TENSES

UNIT 7 QUESTIONS AND PHRASAL VERBS

UNIT 1 THE PRESENT TENSES

◆ 1a ◆ The Simple Present Tense: Statements
Student Book p. 2

1 Practice

Complete the sentences with the correct form of the verbs in parentheses. Make the verbs negative if the word *not* is in the parentheses.

1. Brendan (be) _____ an actor.

2. He (work) _____ in Hollywood.

3. He (not, be) _____ famous.

4. He (not, make) _____ a lot of money, but he (like) _____ his job.

5. He (be) _____ on a TV show. He (play) _____ a college student.

6. Brendan (have) _____ a girl friend.

7. Her name (be) _____ Sheila. She (be) _____ a dancer.

8. Sheila (not, eat) _____ meat or junk food.

9. She (take) _____ dance class on Saturday morning.

10. When she (not, have) _____ a job dancing, she (work) _____

    in a restaurant.

11. They (not, live) _____ together.

12. They (windsurf) _____ almost every day.

2 Practice

Write the letter of the correct negative form in the blanks.

1. Jack ___d___ married, and he ___c___ have any children.

2. Domenic and Theresa _____ home now.

3. Claudia _____ watch TV.

4. I _____ have a large house because I _____ rich.

5. You _____ speak Korean, and I _____ speak Spanish.

6. Letitia _____ hungry, and we _____ thirsty now.

7. You _____ understand. I _____ angry. I'm just tired.

8. Mr. Phillips _____ wear glasses, and he _____ very young.

   a. 'm not   **b.** don't   **c.** doesn't   **d.** isn't   **e.** aren't

3 Practice

Complete the sentences with the correct form of the verbs in parentheses.

Jackie: Debbie, who is this in the photo?

Debbie: Oh, that (be) _____is_____ my boyfriend.
                                     1

Jackie: What's he like?

Debbie: He (be) _____ fun. His name (be) _____ Mark. He (be) _____
                    2   3   4

really interesting. He (live) _____ in Seattle and (teach)
                                    5

_____ at a small college there. He (be) _____ 31. He
          6   7

(have) _____ brown eyes, and he (not, have) _____ a lot
          8   9

of hair. I (think) _____ he (be) _____ really good looking.
                        10   11

He (not, have) _____ a car, so he (ride)
                               12

_____ a bike to work. He (fly) _____
          13   14

to St. Louis every year to visit his dad. He (go) _____ on ski trips every
                                                 15

winter with his friends. We both (enjoy) _____ music. We (call)
                                      16

_____ each other often, and we (talk) _____
          17   18

for an hour. I (be) _____ very happy.
                  19

4 Practice

Complete the sentences using an appropriate verb and the simple present tense.

1. Engineers _build bridges_____.

2. A nurse _____.

3. Police officers _____.

4. A cook _____.

5. A president _____.

6. Students _____.

7. A photographer _____.

8. Birds _____.

9. A pilot _____.

10. A reporter _____.

1b Adverbs of Frequency

Student Book p. 6

5 Practice

Read the sentences about teenagers. Then rewrite the sentences and put the adverbs in the correct position.

1. Teenagers want to be independent.

   (usually) _Teenagers usually want to be independent_.

2. Parents worry about their children.

   (always) _____.

3. Teenagers go to bed before midnight.

   (rarely) _____.

4. Teenagers get part-time jobs.

   (sometimes) _____.

5. Parents want their children to be happy.

   (always) _____.

6. Teenagers tell their parents everything.

   (seldom) _____.

7. Parents are strict with their children.

   (often) _____.

8. Teenagers want to be with their friends.

   (always) _____.

9. Teenagers are interested in music.

   (usually) _____.

10. Parents disagree with their children.

    (sometimes) _____.

11. Teenagers are busy.

    (often) _____.

12. Parents stop loving their children.

    (never) _____.

6 Practice

Write about your parents.

1. My parents always _____ .

2. They rarely _____ .

3. They often _____ .

4. They're sometimes _____ .

5. They're not usually _____ .

6. They never _____ .

7 Practice

Adam and George are talking about a coworker. Put the adverbs in the correct position and use the correct form of the verbs in parentheses.

Adam: Laura (be, always) __is always__ early.
                                                    1

George: I know. And she (take, usually) _____ only half an hour for lunch.
                                                            2

Adam: Yes. She (not, leave, often) _____early, and she
                                                    3

(finish, always) _____ her work.
                            4

George: It's amazing. She (call in, rarely) _____ sick on Monday
                                                            5

and (work, often) _____ late.
                            6

Adam: She (be, usually) _____ helpful to customers.
                                    7

George: She (be, often) _____ at her desk, and she (play,
                                    8

usually) _____ music while she works.
                    9

Adam: And she (talk, never) _____ to her friends on the phone.
                                            10

George: Yeah, she's a really good worker.

8 Practice

Write about you and the people in your class. Use adverbs in your sentences.

1. _David always sits in the front._ (OR) _I'm rarely sick._

2. _____

3. _____

4. _____

5. _____

6. _____

7. _____

8. _____

9. _____

10. _____

1c The Present Progressive Tense: Statements

Student Book p. 9

9 ## Practice

Write *C* next to the verb if it is spelled correctly. Write *I* if it is spelled incorrectly.

_____ **1.** beginning

_____ **2.** happenning

_____ **3.** shoping

_____ **4.** looking

_____ **5.** danceing

_____ **6.** running

_____ **7.** criing

_____ **8.** saying

_____ **9.** doing

_____ **10.** smelling

_____ **11.** eating

_____ **12.** liveing

10 ## Practice

Complete the sentences with the present progressive form of the verbs in parentheses.

A. Today is Fran's birthday. Her friends (plan) _____ a surprise

party for her. They (wait) _____ for Fran to leave. Her friends

(watch) _____ her from across the street.

Joe: What is she doing?

Marilyn: She (watch) _____ TV. Oh, now she (get up)

_____ . She (turn off) _____

the TV. She (put on) _____ her coat. Okay, she (leave)

_____ .

Joe: Good. Let's go. I have the key to her house. Who has the cake?

B. Ken: Where is everyone?

Mari: Well, Tammy (play) _____ soccer. Satchiko (shop)
1

_____ for CDs with her friends, and Nicola (take)
2

_____ a nap. I (make) _____ cookies.
3   4

C. Ben is on a business trip with two coworkers. He (talk) _____
1

to his friend Sarah on the phone.

Ben: Hi, Sarah.

Sarah: Hi! Are you having a good time?

Ben: Yeah, it's okay. Jerry and Eric (watch) _____ baseball,
2

and we (eat) _____ some pizza right now. (*Ben sneezes.*)
3

Sarah: Are you okay?

Ben: Yeah, but I think I (get) _____ a cold.
4

D. A video (play) _____ in the living room. Angela (watch)
1

_____ the video while Allison (make) _____
2   3

popcorn in the kitchen.

Allison: What's happening?

Angela: The girl (cry) _____, and the boy (hold)
4

_____ her hand. Okay, now we (look)
5

_____ at a house. A car (drive)_____ up.
6   7

The girl (get out) _____ of the car and (run)
8

_____ to the door.
9

Allison: Why?

Angela: I don't know! Come in here. You (miss) _____ everything!
10

II Practice

Answer the questions using the present progressive tense.

1. Look outside. What's happening? *A woman is riding a bicycle.*

   Some children are playing basketball.

2. How is the weather? _____.

3. What is happening in your country now? _____.

4. What's happening in the world? _____ .

5. What are your classmates doing? _____ .

12 Practice

Look at the photo. Write sentences using the present progressive tense.

1. _____ .

2. _____ .

3. _____ .

4. _____ .

1d The Simple Present Tense OR The Present Progressive Tense

Student Book p. 13

13 Practice

Complete the sentences. Use the simple present or the present progressive of the verbs in parentheses. Contractions or full forms are correct.

1. I (usually, make) _____ coffee at 7:30, but today is Saturday!

So, I (make) _____ coffee now, even though it is 9:00.

2. On Thursdays, Vivian paints for two hours. Today, Vivian (not, paint)

_____ because she (not, feel) _____ well.

3. **A:** What's Mickey doing?

B: He (try) _____ to stand on his head.

4. Jeff (usually, not, play) _____ soccer, but he (play)

_____ soccer today. He (not, have) _____

many friends, so he (try) _____ to meet people.

14 Practice

Complete the sentences with the simple present or present progressive of the verbs in parentheses.

Many unusual animals (live) _____ in Australia,
1
like the koala, the kangaroo, and the wallaby. Australia (have)

_____ about 20 million people. The people (speak)
2

_____ English, and they (use) _____ the
3 4
Australian dollar. Today, more people (go) _____ to
5
Australia, and tourism (grow) _____.
6

15 Practice

Complete the sentences with the simple present or present progressive of the verbs in parentheses.

Giant pandas (live) _____ only in China. They
1
(eat) _____ bamboo and (usually, not make)
2

_____ many sounds. They (like) _____
3 4
the cold, wet forests in China, and they only (have) _____ one baby a year.
5
They (not, see) _____ well, and an adult male panda (weigh)
6

_____ almost 300 pounds! But the giant panda (be) _____ in
7 8
trouble. Today, the number of giant pandas (get) _____ smaller.
9

16 Practice

Read the sentences. Write *C* next to the sentence if the simple present or the present progressive is used correctly. Write *I* if it is used incorrectly.

_____ **1.** I'm always tired in the morning.

_____ **2.** I'm usually eating breakfast every day.

_____ **3.** People are speaking Portuguese in Brazil.

_____ **4.** Cesare drinks coffee every morning.

_____ **5.** Elizabeth is always talking now.

_____ **6.** Javier is looking out the window.

_____ **7.** Kimberly is always doing her homework at 7:00.

_____ **8.** Yiwen takes a shower now.

_____ **9.** Min is watching TV now.

_____ **10.** Eun Kyung rides her bike today.

1e Nonprogressive Verbs

Student Book p. 15

17 Practice

Read the letter and complete the sentences with the simple present or the present progressive tense.

Dear Hans,

How are you? I (be) _____ in science class right now, but we

(take) _____ a break. I (like) _____ the class,
       2   3

but I (not, understand) _____ the teacher. She (speak, usually)
                                4

_____ too fast.
    5

My other classes (be) _____ fine, and I (know)
                             6

_____ a lot of people now. I (not, have) _____
   7   8

a lot of homework.

Oh, the teacher (start) _____ class again. I (think)
                            9

_____ of you.
   10

Bye,

Carole

18 Practice

Circle the letter of the correct sentence.

1. **a.** Lisa remembers me.
   b. Lisa is remembering me.

2. **a.** I'm not knowing the answer.
   b. I don't know the answer.

3. **a.** I'm hating math.
   b. I hate math.

4. **a.** Debbie likes bowling.
   b. Debbie is liking bowling.

5. **a.** Dinner is smelling good!
   b. Dinner smells good!

See, Look At, Watch, Hear, and Listen To

19 **Practice**

Read the following sentences. Underline the correct verb.

1. **A:** Tina is skating.
   B: Where is she? I (don't look at / don't see) her.

2. Tom, you (don't hear / 're not listening to) me!

3. Jay, please (see / look at) me when I'm talking to you.

4. There's the party. I (hear / listen to) music. It's at that house.

5. I wear glasses because I (don't see / am not looking at) well.

6. On Sunday afternoon, my uncles (watch / see) football.

7. Peggy is daydreaming. She isn't (listening to / hearing) the teacher.

8. A good babysitter (looks at / watches) children carefully.

9. **A:** What are you doing?
   B: I ('m seeing / 'm looking at) the garden.

10. Wake up. I ('m listening to / hear) the baby. She's crying.

11. Steven (doesn't see / doesn't watch) TV.

12. Do you (hear / listen to) the radio in the car?

20 **Practice**

Complete the sentences with *hear, listen to, watch, see,* or *look at*. Use the simple present or the present continuous tense.

1. Uma _____ MTV right now.

2. Tyler _____ music at night.

3. Ho Joon _____ the stars right now.

4. I'm scared. I _____ a noise in the kitchen. I don't know what it is.

5. The girls are home. I _____ them in the driveway getting out of

   the car.

6. Kiomi (not) _____ well. She wears contact lenses.

7. Todd (not) _____ at the blackboard. He _____

   something outside.

8. My cousins _____ Spanish videos every Friday night.

9. Oh, I _____ birds outside. They're singing!

1g Yes/No Questions and Short Answers; Wh- Questions
Student Book p. 20

21 Practice

Write the letter of the correct short answer next to the question.

_____ **1.** Do you work out in the morning?

_____ **2.** Does your aunt live in Australia?

_____ **3.** Are your parents coming with us?

_____ **4.** Is it raining?

_____ **5.** Are Ted and Jasmine having a party?

_____ **6.** Is the water boiling?

_____ **7.** Do you drive to work?

_____ **8.** Does Kim take care of her mother?

        a. Yes, they are.
        b. Yes, she does.
        c. No, I don't.
        d. No, it isn't.

22 Practice

Write short answers to the questions.

1. Are you having fun? _____.

2. Do you ski? _____.

3. Are you listening to music? _____.

4. Do you speak French? _____.

5. Are you sitting in your bedroom? _____.

6. Are you working at your computer? _____.

7. Do you play an instrument? _____.

8. Are you interested in politics? _____ .

9. Do you have any pets? _____ .

10. Do you like English grammar? _____ .

11. Are you working hard? _____ .

12. Are you thinking about a snack? _____ .

23 Practice

Read the information. Then write questions and answers using the prompts.

Tigers are the largest animals in the cat family. Today, there are five different kinds of tigers in the world. Two of them are the Siberian tiger, which lives in eastern Russia, and the Bengal tiger, which lives in India. Siberian tigers are bigger than Bengal tigers because they live in a colder climate. They have thick fur and more fat under their skin. Male Siberian tigers sometimes weigh from 450 to 600 pounds.

Does your cat like to swim? Well, tigers do! Tigers also see very well at night, and they can eat 90 pounds of food at one time. Every tiger has a unique stripe pattern.

1. *Do Siberian tigers live in India?*

No, they don't. They live in eastern Russia.

2. Where _____ ?

_____ .

3. Why _____ ?

_____ .

4. How much do _____ ?

_____ .

5. Do _____ ?

_____ .

24 **Practice**

Write questions and answers in the simple present or the present progressive using the prompts.

1. what/Burt/do/now   _What is Burt doing now_ _____?

   fix/his car   _He's fixing his car_ _____.

2. who/go/store/with you _____?

   Ellen _____.

3. what/Martha/do_____?

   she/be/a police officer _____.

4. when/you/take/a shower/in the morning _____?

   I/take/a shower/at 7:00 _____.

5. who/you/talk to _____?

   I/talk to/my sister _____.

6. what/you/think/about air pollution _____?

   I/think/it's a problem _____

7. what/you/think about _____?

   I/think about/lunch _____!

8. where/you/go/now _____?

   I/go/to the bank _____.

9. where/you/go on Sundays _____?

   I/go to/yoga class _____.

10. what/you/do _____?

    I/send/email _____.

A **Choose the best answer, A, B, C, or D, to complete the sentence. Mark your answer by darkening the oval with the same letter.**

1. Anita _____ smoke.

   A. is not   Ⓐ Ⓑ Ⓒ Ⓓ
   B. doesn't
   C. is
   D. don't

2. It _____ in the summer.

   A. seldom rains   Ⓐ Ⓑ Ⓒ Ⓓ
   B. rain
   C. isn't rain
   D. don't rain

3. Patty _____ in the garden now.

   A. don't work   Ⓐ Ⓑ Ⓒ Ⓓ
   B. doesn't work
   C. works
   D. is working

4. I _____ you!

   A. remember   Ⓐ Ⓑ Ⓒ Ⓓ
   B. am remembering
   C. is remembering
   D. am not remembering

5. Mrs. Kaufman _____ her new neighbor. She's not very friendly.

   A. isn't liking   Ⓐ Ⓑ Ⓒ Ⓓ
   B. don't like
   C. like
   D. doesn't like

6. Gordon is at the museum this afternoon, and he _____ the new sculpture.

   A. is looking at   Ⓐ Ⓑ Ⓒ Ⓓ
   B. see
   C. is watching
   D. is seeing

7. What _____ for dinner?

   A. is you wanting Ⓐ Ⓑ Ⓒ Ⓓ
   B. are you wanting
   C. does you wanting
   D. do you want

8. Fire _____ air, heat, and fuel.

   A. need   Ⓐ Ⓑ Ⓒ Ⓓ
   B. needs
   C. is needing
   D. are needing

9. How much _____?

   A. do elephants weigh   Ⓐ Ⓑ Ⓒ Ⓓ
   B. does elephants weigh
   C. are elephants weighing
   D. weigh elephants

10. My teenage children _____ tired in the evening.

   A. often is   Ⓐ Ⓑ Ⓒ Ⓓ
   B. is often
   C. often are
   D. are often

B Find the underlined word or phrase, A, B, C, or D, that is incorrect. Mark your answer by darkening the oval with the same letter.

1. He <u>usually</u> <u>is</u> <u>calls</u> his mother
        A   B   C

   <u>on Saturday mornings</u>.
         D

   Ⓐ Ⓑ Ⓒ Ⓓ

2. Sharon <u>doesn't</u> <u>speak</u> English, so she
          A   B

   <u>isn't understanding</u> what the <u>newspapers</u>
        C   D

   say.

   Ⓐ Ⓑ Ⓒ Ⓓ

3. Dogs <u>usually</u> <u>aren't</u> <u>like</u> loud noises.
          A   B   C

   <u>Some dogs</u> run away.
      D

   Ⓐ Ⓑ Ⓒ Ⓓ

4. Kevin <u>is</u> <u>usually</u> <u>talking</u> to his children
        A   B   C

   <u>right now</u>.
     D

   Ⓐ Ⓑ Ⓒ Ⓓ

5. Kyle is <u>listen to</u> music and <u>playing</u>
         A   B

   <u>his guitar</u> <u>right now</u>.
     C   D

   Ⓐ Ⓑ Ⓒ Ⓓ

6. Cats <u>don't</u> <u>flying</u>. They also <u>don't</u> <u>like</u>
        A   B   C   D

   to swim.

   Ⓐ Ⓑ Ⓒ Ⓓ

7. When <u>do</u> <u>they</u> usually <u>going</u> to <u>school</u>?
       A   B   C   D

   Ⓐ Ⓑ Ⓒ Ⓓ

8. <u>I</u>'m not <u>having</u> a good time. <u>I</u> <u>go</u>
    A   B   C D

   home now.

   Ⓐ Ⓑ Ⓒ Ⓓ

9. <u>The weather is</u> <u>often</u> very pleasant in the
         A   B

   fall. <u>It</u> rains <u>never</u> in the summer.
       C   D

   Ⓐ Ⓑ Ⓒ Ⓓ

10. <u>Michael</u> <u>has</u> three brothers. <u>He</u>
       A   B   C

    <u>isn't having</u> any sisters.
       D

    Ⓐ Ⓑ Ⓒ Ⓓ

UNIT 2 THE PAST TENSES

2a The Simple Past Tense
Student Book p. 30

1 Practice

Write *C* next to the past tense verb if it is spelled correctly. Write *I* if it is spelled incorrectly.

_____ 1. fixed

_____ 2. worryed

_____ 3. exitted

_____ 4. closed

_____ 5. enjoied

_____ 6. traveled

_____ 7. planned

_____ 8. visited

_____ 9. cleanned

_____ 10. stayed

2 Practice

Complete the sentences using the simple past tense of the verbs in parentheses.

Yesterday, I (need) _____ a cup of coffee,
1

so I (walk) _____ to the coffee shop. The coffee
2

shop is next to the bank. I (stop) _____ in front
3

of the bank to buy a newspaper. Suddenly, the door (open)

_____, and a man in a mask (look)
4

_____ out. He (look) _____ at me
5   6

and (shout) _____, "Get out of my way!" He
7

(push) _____ me and (exit) _____ the bank quickly. I (start)
8   9

_____ to follow him. I (grab) _____ his shoulder, and he (drop)
10   11

_____ a bag of money from the bank. I (pull out) _____ my
12   13

handcuffs and quickly (arrest) _____ him. I (call) _____ my partner,
14   15

and she (arrive) _____ soon after that. The robber (try) _____ to
16   17

escape, but we (push) _____ him into our car.
18

I am a police officer.

3 Practice

Write short answers to the questions.

1. Did you sleep well last night?

   Yes, I did. (OR) _No, I didn't_ .

2. Did you read the newspaper yesterday?

   _____ .

3. Did your best friend call you last night?

   _____ .

4. Did a friend drive you to school last week?

   _____ .

5. Did you go on vacation last year?

   _____ .

6. Did you see any movies last weekend?

   _____ .

7. Did you use a computer today?

   _____ .

8. Did your parents teach you how to ride a bike when you were a child?

   _____ .

4 Practice

Write questions and answers using the prompts.

1. you/play/tennis last summer

   Did you play tennis last summer?

   Yes, I did. (OR) _No, I didn't. I played basketball._

2. your teacher/give/you any homework today

   _____ ?

   _____ .

3. you/understand/the lesson

_____?

_____.

4. your classmates/ask/questions in class

_____?

_____.

5. you/do/something special for your birthday last year

_____?

_____.

6. you/send/any email today

_____?

_____.

7. you/drive/anywhere this week

_____?

_____.

8. you/see/your best friend last weekend

_____?

_____.

9. you/study/for the last test

_____?

_____.

10. you/talk/to your neighbors last week

_____?

_____.

2b Irregular Verbs

Student Book p. 34

5 Practice

Write the present tense form of the following past tense verbs.

have   **1.** had

_____ **2.** went

_____ **3.** sent

_____ **4.** left

_____ **5.** did

_____ **6.** won

_____ **7.** got

_____ **8.** gave

_____ **9.** met

_____ **10.** ate

_____ **11.** became

6 Practice

Complete the sentences with the simple past tense of the verbs in parentheses.

My little brother is such a brat! Two weeks

ago, he (stand) _____ outside my
1

bedroom door and (sing) _____ really
2

loudly. It (drive) _____ me crazy.
3

Then, he (put) _____ one of my
4

shoes in the shower! On Monday, he (not, finish)

_____ his chores, and he (not, do)
5

_____ his homework. Last week, he
6

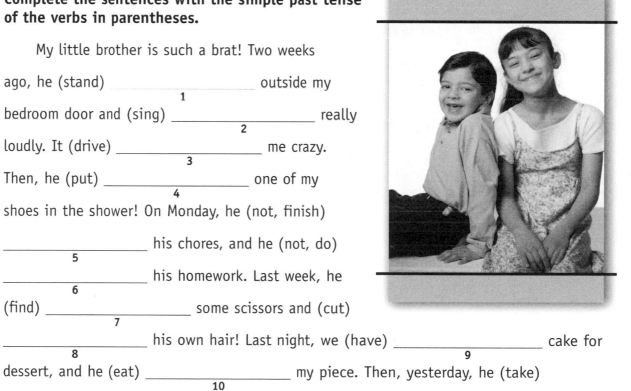

(find) _____ some scissors and (cut)
7

_____ his own hair! Last night, we (have) _____ cake for
8 9

dessert, and he (eat) _____ my piece. Then, yesterday, he (take)
10

_____ my father's keys and (drive) _____ down the block.
11 12

He's ten years old!

7 Practice

Complete the story about Frida Kahlo. Write the correct form of the verbs in parentheses.

Frida Kahlo (be) _____ a famous Mexican painter. She (have)
                              1

_____ a difficult life. She (catch) _____ polio at a very young age,
          2   3

and then a bus accident (cause) _____ her serious pain. She (live)
                                          4

_____ with that pain all her life. She (teach) _____ herself to paint.
          5   6

A mirror (hang) _____ above her bed, so she (paint) _____ many
                        7   8

pictures of herself lying down.

In 1929, she (marry) _____ the already famous Mexican artist, Diego
                              9

Rivera. In 1930, they (go) _____ to San Francisco because Diego (have)
                                  10

_____ a job there. In 1931, they (go) _____ to New York. In 1939,
          11   12

after years of traveling and many problems in their marriage, they (divorce)

_____, but in 1940, they (remarry) _____. She (die)
          13   14

_____ in 1954. Today, her paintings are very popular and valuable.
          15

8 Practice

Write questions and answers using the prompts.

1. Frida/have/easy life

   Did Frida have an easy life?

   No, she didn't.

2. she/catch/polio

   _____?

   _____.

3. car accident/cause/her pain

   _____?

   _____.

4. what/teach/herself

   _____?

   _____.

5. what/hang/above her bed

   _____?

   _____.

6. who/she/marry

   _____?

   _____.

7. when/they/go/to San Francisco

   _____?

   _____.

8. why/they/go/to San Francisco

   _____?

   _____.

9. why/they/divorce

_____?

_____.

10. when/she/die

_____?

_____.

Practice

Write an appropriate question for each answer.

1. A: _What did you do last night?_

    B: I watched TV and then went to bed early.

2. A: _____?

    B: I didn't go anywhere.

3. A: _____?

    B: Yes, they did.

4. A: _____?

    B: No, it isn't.

5. A: _____?

    B: To the airport.

6. A: _____?

    B: I went for a walk.

7. A: _____?

    B: At 6:00 this morning.

8. A: _____?

    B: My cousins.

9. A: _____?

    B: We had a party.

10. A: _____?

    B: Because she drove to work.

10 Practice

Complete the sentences using the simple past tense.

1. Yesterday, I _ate dinner_, but I didn't _eat dessert_.

2. Last summer, I _____, but I didn't _____.

3. Last night, my family didn't _____, but we _____.

4. In class today, my teacher _____,

   but he/she didn't _____.

5. Two weeks ago, my best friend _____, but she/he

   didn't _____.

2c The Past Progressive Tense

Student Book p. 38

11 Practice

Complete the sentences with the past progressive of the verbs in parentheses.

A. At midnight last New Year's Eve, my next-door neighbors (have) _____
1

   a party. Some people (sing) _____ very loudly. My husband and I (watch)
2

   _____ TV, and our daughter (babysit) _____. Our young son
3   4

   (sleep) _____. Outside it (snow) _____, and some teenagers
5   6

   (light) _____ firecrackers.
7

B. I was very busy last summer. I (work) _____ part time and (take)
1

   _____ three classes. I (live) _____ with my parents. They
2   3

   (paint) _____ their house, and I (help) _____ them.
4   5

C. Driver: How fast (I, go) _____?
1

   Police Officer: You (go) _____ 95 miles an hour!
2

D. Andrea: What (you, do) _____ during the power failure last week?
1

   Justin: I (visit) _____ my brother. We (not, do) _____
2   3

             anything special, but everyone in the apartment building

             (wonder) _____ what happened. How about you?
4

   Andrea: I (take) _____ a shower and (wash) _____ my
5   6

             hair.

E. We had a terrible babysitter last Saturday. When we got home, the baby (cry)

_____ , and our oldest son (still, watch) _____ TV. The

      1   2

babysitter (talk) _____ on the phone, her boyfriend (play)

                    3

_____ our children's video games, and something (burn)

      4

_____ in the kitchen!

      5

F. Wei Lin (meet) _____ some friends for dinner last night. She (get)

                    1

_____ money from the ATM. A man (look at) _____ her from

      2   3

across the street. A few minutes later, she (walk) _____ quickly down the

                                          4

street, and the man (follow) _____ her. She (get) _____

                          5   6

worried, so she turned around and looked at him. He (wave) _____ at her

                                                  7

and (call) _____ her name. It was her friend Ron!

            8

12   Practice

Write questions and answers using the prompts.

1. what/you/do/last Saturday at 9:00

   What were you doing last Saturday at 9:00?

   I wasn't doing anything special.

2. who/you/talk to/yesterday/at 2:00

   _____?

   _____.

3. where/you/go/yesterday morning/at 8:30

   _____?

   _____.

4. what/you/think about/today/in class

   _____?

   _____.

5. what/some of your friends/do/last night at 7:30

   _____?

   _____.

2d The Simple Past Tense OR the Past Progressive Tense

Student Book p. 42

13 Practice

Read the sentences. What does each sentence mean? Circle *a* or *b*.

1. When I got hungry, I made dinner.

    a. First I got hungry, and then I made dinner.

    b. I started making dinner, and then I got hungry.

2. When I got hungry, I was making dinner.

    a. First I got hungry, and then I made dinner.

    b. I started making dinner, and then I got hungry.

3. The children were skateboarding when it started to snow.

    a. First it started to snow, and then the children skateboarded.

    b. The children started skateboarding, and then it started to snow.

4. Jay called 911 when he saw the accident.

    a. First he saw the accident, and then he called 911.

    b. He started to call 911, and then he saw the accident.

5. My uncle was painting the house when he fell off the ladder.

    a. First he fell off the ladder, and then he painted the house.

    b. He started painting the house, and then he fell off the ladder.

6. When the lights went out, our husbands were playing cards.

    a. First the lights went out, and then our husbands played cards.

    b. Our husbands started playing cards, and then the lights went out.

7. Monique got sick while she was working at the factory.

    a. First she got sick, and then she worked at the factory.

    b. She started working at the factory, and then she got sick.

8. Patrick was driving home when he heard the news.

    a. First he heard the news, and then he drove home.

    b. He started driving before he heard the news.

9. Patrick drove home when he heard the news.

    a. First he heard the news, and then he drove home.

    b. He started driving before he heard the news.

10. Daniel danced when Mary got to the party.

    a. First Mary got to the party, and then Daniel danced.

    b. Daniel started dancing before Mary got there.

|14| Practice

Complete the sentences with the correct form of the verbs in parentheses.

Galileo Galilei was born in 1564. In 1581, he (go) _____ to the

1
University of Pisa. His father (want) _____ him to study medicine, but he

2
(be) _____ interested in mathematics. He (teach) _____

3   4
mathematics when he (write) _____ his first book, *The Little Balance*.

5

He (not, invent) _____ the

6
telescope, but he (improve) _____

7
it. While he (look at) _____ the

8
sky, he (discover) _____ that the

9
moon has mountains and craters, and he (be)

_____ the first person to see

10
four moons around Jupiter. He (come)

_____ to believe that Earth

11
rotates around the sun, and this

(make) _____ him unpopular

12
with the church.

15 Practice

Complete the sentences about you, your friends, and your family.

1. Last night while I _____, my roommate _____.

2. When I met my best friend, _____.

3. When _____, I cried.

4. _____ when my grandparents came to visit.

5. My classmates laughed when _____.

6. My father _____ when my mother met him.

7. (fill in name) _____ was talking on the phone

   when _____.

8. While _____, the teacher was talking.

9. _____ while I was sleeping last night.

10. While I was online, _____.

2e Past Time Clauses

Student Book p. 44

16 Practice

Complete the sentences.

1. Before I started this practice, _____.

2. _____ after I got home today.

3. After I got up, _____.

4. Before I was born, my parents _____.

5. While I was brushing my teeth last night, _____.

6. _____ when I got to school yesterday.

7. _____ after I went to bed.

8. Before I took this class, _____.

9. _____ when the sun rose today.

10. While I was talking to <name>, I _____.

2f Used To

Student Book p. 46

17 Practice

Complete the sentences using *used to* or *didn't use to* and the verbs in parentheses.

In ancient Egypt, people (write) _____ on paper like ours. Instead, they

wrote on paper made from a plant that grew along the Nile River. They also (make)

_____ boats, rope, and fuel from this reed and roots. This plant was called

"papyrus," and the English word "paper" comes from this word. Because it was so

important, the Egyptians (export) _____ it to many places in the

Mediterranean. Making papyrus (be) _____ a secret, but now we know that

they (cut) _____ down the reed and dry strips of the inside plant into layers.

Then they (make) _____ rolls of 20 sheets each. Papyrus was so important to

the ancient Egyptians, it (be) _____ a symbol of Lower Egypt.

18 Practice

Write sentences with *used to* or *didn't use to* and information from the chart.

Scott – 1988	Scott – Now
• smoked	• doesn't smoke
• lived in L.A.	• lives in Tokyo
• was a waiter	• teaches English
• was married	• is single
• didn't like rap music	• likes rap music
• didn't speak Japanese	• speaks Japanese

1. _Scott used to smoke, but now he doesn't_____.

2. _____.

3. _____.

4. _____.

5. _____.

6. _____.

A **Choose the best answer, A, B, C, or D, to complete the sentence. Mark your answer by darkening the oval with the same letter.**

1. Glen and Jill _____ in Hong Kong when they broke up.

    A. were stay   Ⓐ Ⓑ Ⓒ Ⓓ
    B. were staying
    C. was staying
    D. stayed

2. Han Jong _____ smoke.

    A. use to   Ⓐ Ⓑ Ⓒ Ⓓ
    B. was
    C. used to
    D. were

3. I _____ dinner before I called you.

    A. ate   Ⓐ Ⓑ Ⓒ Ⓓ
    B. eat
    C. eated
    D. was eat

4. While the ship _____, the band was playing.

    A. sank   Ⓐ Ⓑ Ⓒ Ⓓ
    B. sinked
    C. sink
    D. was sinking

5. What _____ you do last summer?

    A. used to   Ⓐ Ⓑ Ⓒ Ⓓ
    B. did
    C. were
    D. do

6. When _____ you using the computer?

    A. did   Ⓐ Ⓑ Ⓒ Ⓓ
    B. was
    C. do
    D. were

7. Who was _____ the music so loudly?

    A. playing   Ⓐ Ⓑ Ⓒ Ⓓ
    B. play
    C. played
    D. used to play

8. They _____ the accident when they looked out the window.

    A. were seeing   Ⓐ Ⓑ Ⓒ Ⓓ
    B. saw
    C. see
    D. used to saw

9. When Professor Wilkinson was teaching at the university, what _____ he discover?

    A. do   Ⓐ Ⓑ Ⓒ Ⓓ
    B. did
    C. was
    D. were

10. I _____ you!

    A. heard   Ⓐ Ⓑ Ⓒ Ⓓ
    B. was hearing
    C. hearing
    D. were hearing

B **Find the underlined word or phrase, A, B, C, or D, that is incorrect. Mark your answer by darkening the oval with the same letter.**

1. The Garcias were <u>have</u> dinner in their
   A

   backyard <u>when</u> <u>it</u> <u>started</u> to rain.
   B   **C**   **D**

2. Yoon <u>was</u> <u>crossing</u> the street <u>when</u> I
   A   **B**   **C**

   <u>sawed</u> him.
   D

3. <u>While</u> Isabelle <u>was</u> <u>taking</u> a shower,
   A   **B**   **C**

   she <u>fall</u>.
   D

4. The president <u>were</u> visiting his parents
   A

   <u>when</u> <u>he</u> <u>heard</u> the news.
   B   **C**   **D**

5. Girls <u>didn't</u> <u>use</u> to be allowed to
   A   **B**

   <u>wearing</u> pants at <u>school</u>.
   C   **D**

   Ⓐ Ⓑ Ⓒ Ⓓ

6. <u>The train</u> was <u>approach</u> the station
   A   **B**

   <u>when</u> Mr. Hendrix <u>got</u> there.
   C   **D**

   Ⓐ Ⓑ Ⓒ Ⓓ

7. Alexander <u>likes</u> soccer <u>now</u>, but he
   A   **B**

   <u>didn't</u> <u>used to</u>.
   C   **D**

   Ⓐ Ⓑ Ⓒ Ⓓ

8. <u>Before</u> she <u>became</u> famous, she <u>use to</u>
   A   **B**   **C**

   <u>drive</u> taxis in New York City.
   D

   Ⓐ Ⓑ Ⓒ Ⓓ

9. <u>While</u> <u>she</u> opened the refrigerator, the
   A   **B**

   <u>butter</u> <u>dropped</u> out.
   C   **D**

   Ⓐ Ⓑ Ⓒ Ⓓ

10. <u>While</u> Rick <u>was</u> <u>working</u>, he <u>haved</u> a
    A   **B**   **C**   **D**

    great idea.

    Ⓐ Ⓑ Ⓒ Ⓓ

UNIT 3 THE FUTURE TENSES

◆ **3a** *Be Going To*

Student Book p. 56

1 Practice

Read the sentences. Write *F* next to the sentence if it is in the future. Write *N* if the sentence is happening now (the present).

_N__ 1. Carrie's shopping for vegetables.

_____ 2. She's going to buy some groceries.

_____ 3. Ing Chul isn't doing her homework right now.

_____ 4. She's going to stay after school.

_____ 5. Ellen and Young are walking to the cafeteria.

_____ 6. They're going to eat dinner.

_____ 7. Michi isn't going to go to college next year.

_____ 8. He's going to work for a plant farm.

_____ 9. I'm not going to the post office now.

_____ 10. I'm going to go there later.

2 Practice

What is going to happen? Complete the sentences with *be going to*.

A. Jackie is reading a book on the couch. Her little brother is sneaking up behind her very quietly. He has a whistle in his hand and a big smile on his face. She doesn't hear him. What is going to happen?

1. Jackie is going to _be angry_____.

2. She isn't going to _____.

3. Her little brother is going to _____.

4. He isn't going to _____.

B. Hiro has his passport and is waiting at the airport. He's happy, but he's also a little nervous.

1. Hiro _____.

2. He (not) _____.

C. Ira is really tired, but he's making cookies now. He falls asleep, and the cookies are still in the oven.

1. The cookies _____.

2. The cookies (not) _____.

3. Ira _____.

4. Ira (not) _____.

D. Today is Sammy's birthday. His friends are hiding in his living room. They have presents and a cake for him. He doesn't know they're there.

1. Sammy _____.

2. His friends _____.

3. Sammy (not) _____.

4. His friends (not) _____.

E. Ted and Janine are engaged to be married next month. Janine isn't happy about this. She wants to wait a little while longer. She asks Ted to meet her for dinner at their favorite restaurant.

1. Janine _____.

2. She (not) _____.

3. Ted _____.

4. He (not) _____.

3 Practice

Read Lisa's to-do list. Write questions and answers using an appropriate verb and *be going to*.

To Do

laundry
bank
haircut
~~mechanic~~
~~dentist~~
groceries
nap
~~library~~

1. *Is she going to do her laundry?*

   Yes, she is.

2. _____?

   _____.

3. _____?

   _____.

4. _____?

   _____.

5. _____?

   _____.

6. _____?

   _____.

7. _____?

   _____.

8. _____?

   _____.

4 Practice

Write questions and answers about you in the future using *be going to* and the prompts.

1. do laundry

   Are you going to do laundry?

   Yes, I am.   (OR)   *No, I'm not.*

2. learn to cook Indian food

   _____?

   _____.

3. teach English

_____?

_____.

4. paint your apartment

_____?

_____.

5. go snowboarding

_____?

_____.

6. use a digital camera

_____?

_____.

7. play in a band

_____?

_____.

3b *Will*

Student Book p. 59

5 Practice

Complete the sentences with _will_ and the verbs in parentheses. You may use contractions or full forms.

1. Mary: Who's going to pick up Dave?

     Stacey: I'm not doing anything. I (do) _'ll do / will do_ it.

2. Will: Tomorrow is my first day of teaching. I'm really nervous.

     Rosemary: Don't worry. You (be) _____ fine.

3. Grandfather to granddaughter:

   You're going to visit New York with your dad. You're going
   to see so many things! You (see) _____
   skyscrapers. You (eat) _____ many different
   foods. You (ride) _____ the subway, and
   you (have) _____ a wonderful time.

4. Mom: Jeff, when are you going to do your homework?

   Jeff: I (do) _____ it after dinner.

5. Oh, man. The bus is late. I (not, have) _____
   time for coffee.

6. Abeer: I'm leaving now.

   Jasmine: Okay. I (see) _____ you tomorrow.

7. Mary Jo: Amy, there's someone at the door.

   Amy: Okay, I (be) _____ right there.

8. Stan: What smells so good? I'm hungry!

   Ivanna: Lasagna. I (get) _____ you some.

9. No! I already told you. I (not, do) _____ it!

10. I'm going to buy a computer, and I predict that my life (change) _____.
    I think that I (do) _____ everything online. I (order) _____
    food online, and the grocer (deliver) _____ the groceries. I (reserve)
    _____ DVDs and (make) _____ reservations for restaurants
    online. I (not, buy) _____ plane or train tickets from the travel agent. I
    (not, pay) _____ bills by mail either. Life (be) _____
    much easier!

11. Cindy: What does your horoscope say?

    Terri: It says that I (have) _____ a good week. I (not, have)
              _____ a lot of money, but a lot of friends
              (call) _____ me.

3c Be Going To OR Will

Student Book p. 62

6 Practice

Write *will* or *be going to* beside each future situation.

1. a plan you made before now _____

2. a prediction for the future _____

3. a future event that is the result of a present situation _____

4. a plan you make right now _____

Write an example of each future situation. Use *will* or *be going to*.

Example: _Karen's going to Paris for her summer vacation_ .

1. _____ .

2. _____ .

3. _____ .

4. _____ .

7 Practice

Complete the sentences with *will* or *be going to* and the verbs in parentheses.

A. Jeremy: I'm having a party on Saturday. I'm asking everyone to bring something.

Liz: Okay. I (bring) _____ potato salad.
                              1

Kurt: I (make) _____ a cake.
                        2

Steve: I (get) _____ the drinks.
                      3

Jeremy: Great. It (be) _____ fun. I (see) _____
                              4   5

you there!

B. Jill: We (go) _____ camping this weekend.
                                    1

    Tim: That sounds like fun.

    Jill: Yeah. We (leave) _____ Friday night.
                                            2

    Tim: Where (go, you) _____?
                                        3

    Jill: We're not sure yet, but we (probably, camp) _____
                                                                    4

    somewhere near the coast.

C. Dolores: I think I (call) _____ the massage therapist to make an
                                        1

    appointment this week.

    Lupe: Why? What's wrong?

    Dolores: Nothing. I (run) _____ the marathon in November, so
                                            2

    I'm training now and sometimes I'm sore after a long run.

    Lupe: That's great. Good luck!

D. Penny: I don't have time to talk right now. I (talk) _____ to

    you tonight. I hope to be home early.

    Marci: Okay.

E. Annie: Are you busy? I (meet) _____ some people at the coffee
                                            1

    shop. Want to come with me?

    Ted: Sure. I (go) _____ with you.
                                    2

F. Mikey: I (be) _____ an artist when I grow up.
                            1

    Courtney: I (be) _____ a doctor.
                                    2

    Luke: I (be) _____ an Olympic ski jumper.
                            3

3d The Present Progressive Tense to Express Future Time

Student Book p. 64

8 **Practice**

Read the sentences. Write *F* next to the sentence if it is in the future. Write *N* if the sentence is happening now (the present).

_____ 1. I'm getting a new computer and returning this one tomorrow.

_____ 2. I'm taking some time off from work next week.

_____ 3. Dad's taking a shower.

_____ 4. He's singing in the shower.

_____ 5. We aren't getting cable TV when we move into the new house.

_____ 6. We're packing now.

_____ 7. My tomatoes aren't doing well.

_____ 8. They're not getting enough sun.

_____ 9. I'm planting lettuce tomorrow.

_____ 10. What are you doing?

_____ 11. What are you doing tonight?

9 **Practice**

Complete the sentences using the present progressive to express the future of the verbs in parentheses.

A. Denise: We (have) _____ a bonfire tonight.

                                     1

Rick: Who (come) _____?

                                   2

Denise: Sally, Devon, Maria, Christopher, and Vince.

Rick: What (bring) _____ everyone _____?

                                   3   (3)

Denise: Well, Vince (bring) _____ corn to cook over the fire.

                                     4

B. Hillary: When (leave) _____ you _____ tomorrow?

Phil: At 9:00.

C. Simon: What (do) _____ you _____ this weekend?

                                  1   (1)

Bill: I (have) _____ my boss over for dinner on Saturday, but on

                                2

Sunday, I (not, do) _____ anything.

                                       3

D. Kyle (enter) _____ college in the fall. He (work) _____

at a summer camp to save money before then. He's a little sad

because his girlfriend (attend) _____ a different school.

10 **Practice**

Jessica Raymond is a famous mystery writer. Read her schedule for tomorrow.

7:00	go over schedule with Jonathon
8:00	work out with trainer
9:00	light breakfast with publicist
10:30–12:00	meeting with accountant
12:00	lunch with editor
2:00–4:00	work
4:30–6:00	book signing
7:00	dinner with family
8:00–11:30	relax at home

She's talking with her assistant Jonathon about her schedule. Complete the sentences with the present progressive to express the future.

Jessica: What (do) _____ I _____ tomorrow?

Jonathon: Well, at 7:00, you _____.

Jessica: And after that?

Jonathon: You _____ at 8:00, and at 9:00, you _____.

Jessica: (meet) _____ I _____ with my accountant?

Jonathon: Yes, from 10:30 to 12:00.

Jessica: Who (have) _____ I _____ lunch with?

Jonathon: Your editor. Then you _____ from 2:00 to 4:00.

Jessica: When (do) _____ I _____ the book signing?

Jonathon: From 4:30 to 6:00.

3e The Simple Present Tense to Express Future Time

Student Book p. 67

II Practice

Look at the cruise ship's itinerary. Then complete the sentences with the verbs in parentheses using the simple present tense to express the future.

Date	Destination	Time
February 6	Miami	5:00 PM
February 7	day at sea	
February 8	Jamaica	7:00 AM – 6:00 PM
February 9	Grand Cayman	9:00 AM – 7:00 PM
February 10	Mexico	8:00 AM – 8:00 PM
February 11	day at sea	
February 12	Miami	11:00 AM

The trip includes a bike tour on Grand Cayman and a shopping trip in Jamaica. Scuba diving lessons are available in Mexico.

Dale: Tell me about your trip. When (leave) _____ you _____?
                                                    1   (1)

Kiomi: We (leave) _____ from Miami on February 6th. We (have) _____ a
                          2   3

day at sea, and then we (arrive) _____ in Jamaica on February 8th.
                                          4

Dale: What (be) _____ your plans there?
                          5

Kiomi: We (shop) _____ and (go) _____ sightseeing. The ship
                          6   7

(depart) _____ Jamaica at 6:00 PM, and it (arrive) _____ in
                 8   9

Grand Cayman the next day. There, we (take) _____ a bike trip. On
                                                        10

February 10th, we (have) _____ a day in Mexico, and we (learn)
                                  11

_____ how to scuba dive.
        12

Then the ship (have) _____
                              13

one last day at sea, and we (return)

_____ to Miami on the
        14

12th.

Dale: Sounds like fun!

12 Practice

Think about your plans this weekend. Write them using *be going to*, the present progressive, or the simple present tense.

1. a. _I'm going to go to a party_ .

   b. _I'm going to a party_ .

   c. _At 7:00 on Saturday, I go to a party_ .

2. a. _____ .

   b. _____ .

   c. _____ .

3. a. _____ .

   b. _____ .

   c. _____ .

3f The Future Conditional

Student Book p. 69

13 Practice

Read the following sentences. Circle the condition and underline the result.

1. <u>Sylvie will make cookies</u> (if she has any chocolate chips.)

2. She'll bring them to the party if she has enough.

3. If she brings enough cookies, everyone will be happy.

4. If there aren't enough cookies, some people will be disappointed.

5. She'll make more cookies if people ask her.

14 Practice

Complete the sentences using the simple present tense or *will* and the verbs in parentheses.

1. If I (make) _____ a lot of money, I (get) _____ a big house and car.

2. I (have) _____ a lot of parties if (live) _____ in a big house.

3. I (be) _____ popular if I (have) _____ a lot of parties.

4. If I (be) _____ popular, I (have) _____ a lot of influence.

5. I (take) _____ on more responsibilities if I (have) _____ a lot of influence.

6. If I (have) _____ more responsibilities, I (be) _____ very busy.

7. I (not, be) _____ happy if I (be) _____ too busy.

8. If I (not, be) _____ happy, I (get) _____ depressed.

15 Practice

Complete the sentences using the simple present tense or *will* and an appropriate verb.

1. If I'm successful, _____.

2. _____ if I don't finish school.

3. If the world stays the same, _____.

4. _____ if violence doesn't stop.

5. If _____, people will live longer.

6. If I speak English fluently, _____.

7. If _____, I won't make the same mistakes.

8. Air pollution will decrease if _____.

9. If I stop watching TV, _____.

10. If _____, I'll exercise more.

3g Future Time Clauses

Student Book p. 71

16 Practice

Write *C* next to the sentence if the result and condition are correct. Write *I* if the result and condition are incorrect.

_____ 1. When Dale will pick up his son, they'll go to the grocery store.

_____ 2. As soon as Doug gets home, he walk his dog.

_____ 3. Rose will take a nap after she eats lunch.

_____ 4. You'll want to put the ice cream in the freezer when you get home.

_____ 5. Everyone will present his/her work before we leave today.

_____ **6.** When you know the assignment, will you call me?

_____ **7.** Hae Jung will be in Paris after she's in Rome.

_____ **8.** If we will find a babysitter, we'll attend the concert.

_____ **9.** The Lees will leave as soon as the wedding will be over.

_____ **10.** If you eat that, you won't sleep well.

| 17 | Practice

Complete the sentences using information from the recipe.

How to Make a Vanilla Milkshake

1. Put two scoops of good vanilla ice cream in a blender.

2. Fill the blender almost to the top with milk.

3. Turn on the blender and blend slowly.

4. Pour the milkshake into a large glass and enjoy.

5. You can add chocolate syrup, fruit, and nuts if you like.

1. Before _*you add the milk*_ , put the ice

   cream in the blender.

2. _____ after you turn on the blender.

3. Before you pour the milkshake into a glass, _____.

4. _____ after you pour the milkshake into a glass.

18 Practice

Describe a process using the prompts.

How to _____

1. Before _____ ,

   _____ .

2. _____ as soon as

   _____ .

3. _____ after

   _____ .

4. When _____ ,

   _____ .

19 Practice

Complete the sentences.

1. When I finish this exercise, _____ .

2. _____ before I go to school tomorrow.

3. When I have enough money, _____ .

4. _____ as soon as I

   _____ .

5. _____ after

   _____ .

SELF-TEST

A   **Choose the best answer, A, B, C, or D, to complete the sentence. Mark your answer by darkening the oval with the same letter.**

1. _____ people don't recycle, there'll be more problems in the environment.

   A. After ⒶⒷⒸⒹ
   B. If
   C. Before
   D. When

2. Sarah's plane _____ at noon.

   A. departs ⒶⒷⒸⒹ
   B. will departs
   C. going to depart
   D. is depart

3. If Max shaves his head, his girlfriend _____ furious!

   A. will ⒶⒷⒸⒹ
   B. is
   C. going to be
   D. will be

4. Jason will study history _____ he doesn't get into law school.

   A. after ⒶⒷⒸⒹ
   B. if
   C. before
   D. when

5. He'll feel better if he _____.

   A. is going to exercise ⒶⒷⒸⒹ
   B. will exercise
   C. exercises
   D. is exercise

6. Tommy and Ashley _____ married next week.

   A. get ⒶⒷⒸⒹ
   B. will get
   C. are getting
   D. going to get

7. As soon as Julie _____ her children, she'll kiss them.

   A. will see ⒶⒷⒸⒹ
   B. is seeing
   C. is going to
   D. sees

8. Who _____ with us to the beach on Saturday?

   A. is coming ⒶⒷⒸⒹ
   B. will come
   C. comes
   D. going to come

9. Dr. Learner _____ to his staff after his last patient tomorrow.

   A. talks ⒶⒷⒸⒹ
   B. will talks
   C. is going to
   D. is talking

10. After Candace _____ the picture, they'll take a break.

    A. is hanging ⒶⒷⒸⒹ
    B. will hang
    C. hangs
    D. is going to hang

B **Find the underlined word or phrase, A, B, C, or D, that is incorrect. Mark your answer by darkening the oval with the same letter.**

1. Myra and Steve <u>going</u> to the hardware
A
store. <u>They</u> <u>intend</u> <u>to repair</u> their
B   C   D
front door.

Ⓐ Ⓑ Ⓒ Ⓓ

2. Roberto <u>meets</u> <u>us</u> at the theater <u>in</u>
A   B   C
<u>two hours</u>.
D

Ⓐ Ⓑ Ⓒ Ⓓ

3. The Clarks <u>leave</u> tomorrow at 8:00
A
because their plane <u>is depart</u> at 9:30.
B
They <u>don't</u> <u>want</u> to be late.
C   D

Ⓐ Ⓑ Ⓒ Ⓓ

4. <u>After</u> Nancy <u>will send</u> email, <u>she'll</u> <u>fax</u>
A   B   C   D
the brochure.

Ⓐ Ⓑ Ⓒ Ⓓ

5. By the year 2020, <u>people</u> <u>aren't use</u> cars
A   B
anymore. <u>They'll</u> <u>ride</u> small scooters.
C   D

Ⓐ Ⓑ Ⓒ Ⓓ

6. Charlotte <u>won't</u> time <u>to see</u> you
A   B
<u>this morning</u>. <u>She's</u> already late.
C   D

Ⓐ Ⓑ Ⓒ Ⓓ

7. In the future, children <u>study</u> at home
A
because <u>schools</u> <u>won't</u> <u>exist</u>.
B   C   D

Ⓐ Ⓑ Ⓒ Ⓓ

8. <u>If</u> Vern <u>finishes</u> the repairs, <u>he</u> <u>starts work</u>
A   B   C   D
in the yard.

Ⓐ Ⓑ Ⓒ Ⓓ

9. You <u>going</u> <u>to love</u> my <u>brother</u>. <u>He's</u>
A   B   C   D
hilarious!

Ⓐ Ⓑ Ⓒ Ⓓ

10. Melissa <u>returns</u> at 10:00. <u>She's</u>
A   B
<u>going to be</u> at the hotel later.
C
We <u>see</u> her then.
D

Ⓐ Ⓑ Ⓒ Ⓓ

UNIT 4 NOUNS, ARTICLES, AND QUANTITY

4a Singular and Plural Nouns

Student Book p. 80

1 Practice

Write C next to the word if the singular or plural is correct. Write I if the singular or plural is incorrect.

_I_ 1. leafs

_____ 2. photos

_____ 3. a children

_____ 4. tomatoes

_____ 5. glasses

_____ 6. a orange

_____ 7. a men

_____ 8. a tornado

_____ 9. a woman

_____ 10. countries

_____ 11. an echo

_____ 12. a foot

_____ 13. parties

_____ 14. a animal

_____ 15. an mouse

2 Practice

Lydia and Susan have just moved into a new apartment. Complete the sentences with the correct plural of the word in parentheses.

Lydia: Where are the (dish) _____?
                                    1

Susan: They're in those (box) _____.
                                    2

Lydia: Okay. I'm putting the (knife) _____ in the drawer over here.
                                    3

Susan: I'll put the (glass) _____ on the shelf.
                                    4

Lydia: We need new (pot) _____ and (pan) _____. These are too old.
                            5   6

Susan: And we need clean (sponge) _____ for the kitchen. I'll make a
                                    7

shopping list.

Lydia: Okay. I'll go to the store. I'm hungry. Are you?

Susan: Yes.

Lydia: I'll pick up some (sandwich) _____ and (soda) _____.
                                    8   9

3 Practice

Sara is a meteorologist. Read her weather report and complete the sentences with the correct plural of the word in parentheses.

There was some unusual weather around the world this past week. In Martinique, two

(volcano) _____ erupted at the same time. People left their (home)
                    1

_____ in (bus) _____.
        2   3

Closer to home, a series of (tornado) _____ raced across much of the
                                                    4

country. They sent (man) _____, (woman) _____, and (child)
                                  5   6

_____ to basements for safety. The wind blew down several (house)
        7

_____, and many homes lost (roof) _____.
        8   9

4 Practice

Complete the sentences with the correct plural of the words in parentheses.

Blaine enjoys living in the country. He can sit on his porch with his dog and look out

at the (cow) _____ and (sheep) _____ in the field. His (chicken)
                    1   2

_____ are running around the yard, and (horse) _____ are in the
        3   4

barn. His (cat) _____ are in the house. (Wolf) _____ and (mouse)
                        5   6

_____ roam through the woods.
        7

4b Nouns as Subjects, Objects, and Objects of Prepositions

Student Book p. 84

5 Practice

Read the sentence. Then read each statement about the sentence and write *C* next to the statement if it is correct. Write *I* if it is incorrect.

The children are riding the Ferris wheel at the fair.

_____ **1.** *The Ferris wheel* is the subject.

_____ **2.** *At* is a preposition.

_____ **3.** *The children* is the object.

_____ **4.** *The fair* is the object of the preposition.

6 Practice

Label the subject (S), verb (V), object (O), preposition (P), and the object of the preposition (OP) in the following sentences.

1. Some children are playing games near the Ferris wheel.

2. Some people are eating cotton candy on a stick.

3. We're watching acrobats on a tightrope.

4. Francie won a giant toy airplane for her daughter.

5. I'm making lunch for the kids.

6. I put the sandwiches on the table.

7. The children are taking a nap after lunch.

Practice

Write sentences, putting the words in the correct order. Then label the sentence parts as in Practice 6. Pay special attention to questions.

1. the onions/the sink/Carol/at/cut

   Carol cut the onions at the sink .
      S   V   O   P   OP

2. put/she/the oven/the lasagna/in

   _____ .

3. dinner/after/we/the dishes/do/wash

   _____ ?

4. us/called/the bank/from/David

   _____ .

5. are buying/the corner market/at/you/vegetables

   _____ ?

6. his veterinarian/from/is eating/Sammy/special food

   _____ ?

7. bought/from/he/my brother/a set of knives

   _____ .

8. to/her parents/them/the beach/took

   _____ .

9. the guests/the party/did/follow/to/the directions

   _____ ?

10. Monday/I/on/have/a dentist's appointment

    _____ .

11. in/a label/does/need/the package/its corner

    _____ ?

12. the clock/on/hung/the wall/ they

    _____ .

4c Count Nouns and Noncount Nouns

Student Book p. 86

8 Practice

Write C if the noun is a count noun. Write N if the noun is a noncount noun.

_____ 1. fork

_____ 2. weather

_____ 3. clouds

_____ 4. rain

_____ 5. tornadoes

_____ 6. food

_____ 7. cheese

_____ 8. milk

_____ 9. bottles

_____ 10. cards

_____ 11. information

_____ 12. smoke

_____ 13. cigarettes

_____ 14. money

_____ 15. dollars

_____ 16. mail

_____ 17. letters

_____ 18. email

_____ 19. exercises

_____ 20. homework

9 Practice

Complete the conversations with the correct form of the nouns in parentheses. Use the singular form for noncount nouns. Use the plural form for count nouns.

A. At a bank, Mr. Hopkins is applying for a loan.

I have two (child) _____ , and I'm helping to pay for their (education)
     1

_____ . They both go to good (university) _____ . They
     2   3

both have (job) _____ , but they don't make enough (money)
     4

_____ to pay for all of their (expense) _____ . Their
     5   6

(happiness) _____ is very important to me.
     7

B. Lily: What did you have for lunch?

Tom: I had (soup) _____ and (cracker) _____ . For
     1   2

dessert, I had (fruit) _____ and (cookie) _____ .
     3   4

C. Ms. Cone: Why did you move to Florida?

Mr. Jeter: I hated the (weather) _____
                                              1
back home. I was sick of (snow)

_____, (wind)
            2
_____, and (ice)
            3
_____. Here there's
            4
no (smog) _____ or (pollution)
                          5
_____, just good clean (air)
            6
_____, (sunshine) _____, (sand)
            7   8
_____, and (water) _____.
            9   10

D. A stylist to a customer at a hair salon:

Stylist: Your hair is really dry! How do you take care of it?

Customer: I wash it with (soap) _____.
                                        1
Stylist: You need to use (shampoo) _____ and (conditioner)
                                              2
_____. I'll treat it today with hot (oil) _____.
            3   4

E. Brad: What's your favorite subject?

Scott: I like (history) _____. What about you?
                                1
Brad: I like (biology) _____, but I'm interested in a lot of
                                2
(subject) _____.
                      3

F. This is fat-free (ice cream) _____. We'll lose (weight)
                                                1
_____ without the (guilt) _____ about eating a lot of it.
            2   3

G. Two roommates to a police officer:

Elizabeth: They took my (jewelry) _____, (money) _____,
                                              1   2
and good (luggage) _____.
                                3

Police Officer: Anything else?

Jane: I think that's it. They left the two (television) _____ and
                                                                      1
the two (laptop) _____, but they destroyed my expensive
                                2
(rug) _____ and (furniture) _____.
                3   4

H. Diplomat's speech at a special party:

We are experiencing (peace) _____ for the first time in many years, and
<u>1</u>

there is much (progress) _____ in (technology) _____.
<u>2</u> <u>3</u>

We are now the world leader in producing (steel) _____, so there are
<u>4</u>

many (job) _____ and a lot of (work) _____ for our people.
<u>5</u> <u>6</u>

We don't have much (poverty) _____, and the general (health)
<u>7</u>

_____ of all citizens is getting better and better.
<u>8</u>

10 Practice

Write as many nouns as you can for the following categories.

Things in your room

laptop

CDs

_____

_____

_____

_____

Things you want in your future

_____

_____

_____

_____

Things in your kitchen

_____

_____

_____

_____

4d A, An, and Some

Student Book p. 90

11 Practice

Write *C* next to the phrase if *a, an,* or *some* is correct. Write *I* if *a, an,* or *some* is incorrect.

_____ **1.** a money

_____ **2.** a dollar

_____ **3.** some gasoline

_____ **4.** an eggs

_____ **5.** an advice

_____ **6.** some knowledge

_____ **7.** a games

_____ **8.** some fun

_____ **9.** an exercise

_____ **10.** a homework

_____ **11.** a mail

_____ **12.** some ice cream

_____ **13.** some work

_____ **14.** a class

12 Practice

Write sentences, putting the words in the correct order.

1. a/food/some/they/in/put/basket

_____*They put some food in a basket*_____.

2. for/Kerry/furniture/apartment/some/bought/an

_____.

3. an/mail/envelope/in/I/the/put/

_____.

4. iron/there/steel/an/is/some/and/automobile/in

_____.

5. cold/he/he/and/some/a/has/needs/medicine

_____.

13 Practice

Complete the sentences with *a, an,* or *some*.

A. Ann: I'm going to sell my car, and I need to clean it out.

Bob: What's in it?

Ann: In the trunk, there's _____ oil, _____ water,
$\qquad$ 1 $\qquad$ 2

_____ spare tire, and _____ flashlight. In the front,
$\qquad$ 3 $\qquad$ 4

there's _____ map, _____ gum, _____
$\qquad$ 5 $\qquad$ 6 $\qquad$ 7

paper, and _____ pen.
$\qquad$ 8

B. Maria: What are you taking on your trip?

Domingo: I'm taking _____ suitcase, _____ clothes,
$\qquad$ 1 $\qquad$ 2

_____ umbrella, _____ jacket, _____
$\qquad$ 3 $\qquad$ 4 $\qquad$ 5

watch, and _____ cologne.
$\qquad$ 6

C. Laurie: Wow. There's nothing to eat in your refrigerator.

Kathy: I know. I need to go shopping. Let's see... there's _____ brown
$\qquad$ 1

lettuce, _____ egg, _____ old frozen pizza,
$\qquad$ 2 $\qquad$ 3

_____ ice cream, _____ tofu, and _____
$\qquad$ 4 $\qquad$ 5 $\qquad$ 6

old orange. Yuck. Let's go out.

4e *Some, Any, Much, Many, A Little, A Few,* and *A Lot Of*
Student Book p. 92

14 Practice

**Complete the conversations with *some, any, much, many, a little, a few,* or *a lot of*.
More than one answer may be possible.**

A. Margaret is talking to her friend Suzanne about her new house.

Margaret: I love the place! There are _____ nice neighbors, and there
$\qquad$ 1

isn't _____ traffic.
$\qquad$ 2

Suzanne: Are there _____ parks?
$\qquad$ 3

Margaret: Yes. And there isn't _____ crime or noise. There are
$\qquad$ 4

_____ restaurants and _____ markets.
$\qquad$ 5 $\qquad$ 6

B. Dennis: How was your vacation?

Rod: We didn't have _____ fun. There was _____
                                       1   2

rain, and there wasn't _____ sun.
                                                3

C. Keith is a car salesman, and he's getting his yearly job performance review. He is not having a good year.

Boss: Keith, you're not having _____ luck this year.
                                                 1

Keith: I know.

Boss: You have _____ knowledge and _____
                                      2   3

experience.

Are you having _____ other problems?
                                         4

Keith: No, not really.

Boss: Do you need _____ time off? Do you need
                                        5

_____ help?
                6

Keith: No, thanks. Business will get better.

15 Practice

Read the facts about Rapa Nui. Write sentences using the information, the words, and *some, any, much, many, a little, a few,* **or** *a lot of.*

Facts about Rapa Nui (Easter Island)
Population:	3000
Size:	160 square km
Industry:	tourism and wool export (15,000 tourists/year)
Jobs:	farming, raising sheep for wool
National affiliation:	Chile
Government:	citizens do not pay taxes
Languages:	Spanish and Rapanui
Moais (head statues):	600
Height of Moais:	3-12 m (10-14 ft.)
Weight of Moais:	some Moais are over 50 tons

jobs	land	Moais	people	tourism	tourists	wool

1. <u>*There is a lot of / some tourism on Rapa Nui.*</u>
2. _____ .
3. _____ .
4. _____ .
5. _____ .
6. _____ .
7. _____ .

4f *Few, A Few, Little,* and *A Little*
Student Book p. 94

16 Practice

Write *C* next to the phrase if *few, a few, little,* or *a little* is used correctly. Write *I* if *few, a few, little,* or *a little* is used incorrectly.

——— **1.** a little clothing   ——— **6.** little weight

——— **2.** a few shoes   ——— **7.** a few advice

——— **3.** few homework   ——— **8.** a little information

——— **4.** a little questions   ——— **9.** a little ideas

——— **5.** few people   ——— **10.** a few beauty

17 Practice

Complete the sentences with *a few, few, a little,* or *little.*

1. I'm thirsty. I need _____ water.

2. It rained a lot last week. The garden needs _____ water.

3. Nadine: Are you hungry?

     Karl: _____. I only had some toast earlier today.

4. Office worker: I need _____ help. My printer isn't printing.

     Computer technician: We're having _____ problems with the network today.

5. Daphne: No one came to the party.

     Murray: _____ people knew about it.

6. Hyung: Do you want to come with me?

   Jae: Sure. I need _____ minutes to get ready.

   Hyung: That's okay. I need _____ time, too.

7. This room is very dull. It needs _____ color.

8. Their son doesn't like school. There are _____ subjects he enjoys.

9. It was very hot last night. I got _____ sleep, so I'm really tired today.

10. Doctor: Does it hurt?

   Patient: Not really. There's _____ pain.

11. Eat _____ vegetables, but _____ butter and sugar.

12. We're going to be in Hawaii, so don't take a lot. You need _____

   clothing—just a swimsuit, shorts, and t-shirts.

13. Adam: How's business?

   Tom: Pretty good. I have _____ clients now.

14. They canceled the class. _____ students came.

15. I'm finishing my homework. I have _____ pages to read.

16. Let's go for a walk. I need _____ exercise.

17. Andrew isn't very popular. He has _____ friends. I think he's lonely.

4g   Units of Measure with Nouns
Student Book p. 96

18   Practice

**Write C next to the phrase if the quantity with the noncount noun is correct.
Write I if the quantity with the noncount noun is incorrect.**

_____ **1.** a tube of information   _____ **6.** a head of toilet paper

_____ **2.** a slice of chips   _____ **7.** three cups of sugar

_____ **3.** a can of soup   _____ **8.** a piece of water

_____ **4.** a carton of jam   _____ **9.** a bottle of water

_____ **5.** a can of lettuce   _____ **10.** a bar of soap

19 Practice

You're going to make dinner for friends. You're serving salad, spaghetti, garlic bread, and fruit. Complete the shopping list with units of measure. More than one answer may be correct.

1. _____ spaghetti

2. _____ tomatoes

3. _____ lettuce

4. _____ tomato sauce

5. _____ cheese

6. _____ carrots

7. _____ bread

8. _____ garlic

9. _____ grapes

10. _____ oranges

4h ◆ Possessive Nouns

Student Book p. 98

20 Practice

Read the following possessive phrases. If the possessive is plural, write *P* next to the phrase. If the possessive is singular, write *S*.

_____ 1. the woman's shoes

_____ 2. the women's shoes

_____ 3. my son's soccer game

_____ 4. my daughters' skates

_____ 5. the students' complaints

_____ 6. the artist's paintings

_____ 7. the artists' paintings

_____ 8. the children's room

_____ 9. the child's room

_____ 10. my parents' TV

21 Practice

Add apostrophes in the correct place to the underlined nouns to show possession.

This is our <u>childrens</u> school. These are the
₁

<u>students</u> desks, this is the <u>teachers</u> lounge, and
₂ ₃

here are the <u>schools</u> computers. Oh, there's a
₄

<u>childs</u> jacket on the floor. There are eight levels
₅

in the school. The upper <u>levels</u> rooms are over
₆

here, and the lower <u>levels</u> rooms are down the hall.
₇

But there is a problem. The <u>schools</u> roof is
₈

leaking, and the <u>students</u> textbooks are old. We
₉

need to change a few things here. Our <u>childrens</u> education is very important.
₁₀

22 Practice

Rewrite the sentences to show possession.

1. These are the fashions of this year.

   These are this year's fashions _____.

2. I disagree with the opinions of the newspapers.

   _____.

3. Did you see the new menus of the two restaurants last week?

   _____?

4. We studied the movies of Alfred Hitchcock.

   _____.

5. Those are the designs of Nancy.

   _____.

6. I don't know the name of my teacher.

   _____.

7. Today is the birthday of my twin sisters.

   _____.

8. Oh, there's the cat of my neighbor.

   _____.

4i ◆ A, An, or The

Student Book p. 100

23 **Practice**

Complete the sentences with _the, a,_ or _an._

A. It is Roberta's birthday. Her best friend, Chloe, bought _____ ring for her. Chloe

   1

   and Roberta went to _____ restaurant. _____ restaurant was near

   2   3

   Chloe's house. In _____ restaurant, she gave _____ ring to her friend.

   4   5

B. Baseball is _____ popular sport. There is _____ baseball field in our

   1   2

   park. A lot of people meet in _____ park every weekend. There's going to be

   3

   _____ baseball game today. We're going to _____ game in an hour.

   4   5

C. Here's how to make _____ omelet. You'll need three eggs, _____

   1   2

   quarter cup of cream, and some salt and pepper. Break _____ eggs into

   3

   _____ bowl. Mix them well, and add _____ cream and salt and

   4   5

   pepper. Put some oil in _____ small frying pan on the stove. When

   6

   _____ pan is hot, put _____ egg mixture in it. Cook it.

   7   8

D. Luis takes his car to _____ garage on Division Street. _____

   1   2

   people there are great. Last summer, he needed _____ new tire. They gave

   3

   him _____ tire at a really good price.

   4

E. Raymond has _____ new cell phone and _____ new number.

   1   2

   _____ phone is very small and _____ number is easy to

   3   4

   remember.

F. I had _____ really bad day yesterday. I got in _____ car accident

   1   2

   and was late to work. Then I bought _____ cup of coffee. I put

   3

   _____ cup on my desk, and then I hit it with my hand. _____

   4   5

   cup fell, and _____ coffee got on my clothes and shoes. I was happy when

   6

   _____ day was over.

   7

G. Janine: What did you get?

Frank: I got some apples, _____ loaf of bread, _____ bottle
1 2
of milk, _____ orange, and _____ bag of chips.
3 4

Janine: Great. Please put _____ apples and _____ orange on
5 6
the counter. _____ milk goes in the refrigerator, and
7
_____ loaf of bread goes in the freezer. I'll take
8
_____ chips.
9

H. Kyle: What did you get for graduation?

Alex: I got _____ new laptop, some money, and some new shoes. I'm
1
taking _____ laptop with me to the dorm next year. I put
2
_____ money in the bank, and I'm wearing _____ new shoes.
3 4

I. Claudine: Have you seen Jose's new house?

Paula: Yes. It's really big. There are two bathrooms. _____ one upstairs
1
is very big and light. _____ one downstairs is smaller.
2
_____ kitchen is very modern, and _____ living room
3 4
connects _____ family room to _____ dining room.
5 6
_____ front yard is nice, too.
7

J. Scott: That was _____ interesting presentation.
1

Elaine: Thank you. Do you think _____ graphics were too complicated?
2

Scott: No. They were fine.

Elaine: Did you understand

_____ statistics?
3

Scott: Yes. And I think _____
4
charts were very clear. You're

going to be _____
5
excellent chairperson of our

group.

4j ◆ Generalizations

Student Book p. 102

24 Practice

Write C next to the sentence if *the* is used correctly. Write I if *the* is used incorrectly.

___I___   **1.** The computers are very useful.

___C___   **2.** The computers at school are slow.

_____   **3.** Let's have Chinese food.

_____   **4.** The Chinese food at that restaurant is delicious.

_____   **5.** Robin eats the chocolate.

_____   **6.** The chocolate from Europe is very good.

_____   **7.** The apples in the bowl are old.

_____   **8.** Corey doesn't eat the apples.

_____   **9.** Teenagers love the music.

_____   **10.** I don't like the music he listens to in the car.

25 Practice

Complete the sentences with *the* or X (no article).

1. We need to buy _____ tomatoes because _____ tomatoes in the garden are still green.

2. Mick doesn't eat _____ meat.

3. _____ meat that they sell at that store isn't fresh.

4. _____ money isn't very important to me.

5. He can barely live on _____ money he makes.

6. I don't usually like _____ carrots, but _____ carrots in this salad are good.

7. Seung Wan dislikes _____ cold weather. _____ weather in his country is mild.

8. Mrs. Harris bought a bag of sugar this morning. She's using _____ sugar in the bowl before she opens _____ new bag.

9. Man Wen doesn't usually wear _____ perfume, but _____ perfume she's wearing tonight is very nice.

10. _____ cars run on _____ gasoline.

11. _____ birds have _____ feathers.

12. _____ books in that shop are expensive.

13. I don't like _____ homework, but _____ homework we had last night was easy.

14. Jennifer loves shopping for _____ clothes.

15. _____ paper comes from _____ trees.

16. Mr. Jacobs trimmed _____ trees in his yard. They were too big.

[26] Practice

Complete the sentences with your own ideas.

1. I ___*always listen to hip-hop*___ music. The music my parents listen to ___*is really old*___.

2. I _____ noise. The noise at my house _____.

3. Traffic _____. The traffic in my town _____.

4. Animals _____. The animals in the wildlife reserve _____.

5. Friends _____. The friends I have _____.

6. Air pollution _____. The air pollution in my country _____.

7. Television shows _____. The television shows I watch _____.

8. Public transportation _____. The public transportation in my town _____.

A **Choose the best answer, A, B, C, or D, to complete the sentence. Mark your answer by darkening the oval with the same letter.**

1. The Herberts have three _____.

   A. child   Ⓐ Ⓑ Ⓒ Ⓓ
   B. children
   C. son
   D. daughter

2. Judith wants to go to the _____.

   A. women's department Ⓐ Ⓑ Ⓒ Ⓓ
   B. woman's department
   C. womens' department
   D. womans' department

3. There isn't _____ money.

   A. some   Ⓐ Ⓑ Ⓒ Ⓓ
   B. an
   C. many
   D. any

4. She doesn't want _____ apple.

   A. some   Ⓐ Ⓑ Ⓒ Ⓓ
   B. a
   C. an
   D. few

5. I want a piece of _____.

   A. milk   Ⓐ Ⓑ Ⓒ Ⓓ
   B. cake
   C. toothpaste
   D. soup

6. It's dry and hot here. This place gets _____ rain.

   A. little   Ⓐ Ⓑ Ⓒ Ⓓ
   B. a little
   C. few
   D. a few

7. The doctors don't need _____ time.

   A. a few   Ⓐ Ⓑ Ⓒ Ⓓ
   B. few
   C. much
   D. many

8. Are you going to the store? I need a loaf of _____.

   A. gasoline   Ⓐ Ⓑ Ⓒ Ⓓ
   B. bread
   C. soap
   D. toilet paper

9. The _____ name is Dawn.

   A. girls   Ⓐ Ⓑ Ⓒ Ⓓ
   B. girls'
   C. girl
   D. girl's

10. Our assistant can go to the coffee shop. He has _____ time.

   A. little   Ⓐ Ⓑ Ⓒ Ⓓ
   B. a little
   C. few
   D. a few

B **Find the underlined word or phrase, A, B, C, or D, that is incorrect. Mark your answer by darkening the oval with the same letter.**

1. The couple went to a lot of partys
      A   B   C
   last year.
       D

   Ⓐ Ⓑ Ⓒ Ⓓ

2. I want to have a little fun, so I need
           A   B   C
   a few money.
    D

   Ⓐ Ⓑ Ⓒ Ⓓ

3. My sister's names are Amanda and Kelly.
        A   B
   My brother's name is Nate.
        C   D

   Ⓐ Ⓑ Ⓒ Ⓓ

4. I'm making a few progress. Now I
            A   B
   understand most of the homework.
           C   D

   Ⓐ Ⓑ Ⓒ Ⓓ

5. We've got a few problems. We need to talk
           A   B
   for a little minutes.
      C   D

   Ⓐ Ⓑ Ⓒ Ⓓ

6. The men needed some information, and
       A   B   C
   the counselor gave them an advice.
                    D

   Ⓐ Ⓑ Ⓒ Ⓓ

7. The volunteers bought some food, but
             A   B   C
   they forgot the roll of peanut butter.
           D

   Ⓐ Ⓑ Ⓒ Ⓓ

8. Charles's opinion is like mine. That family
    A
   needs a help and some happiness.
        B   C   D

   Ⓐ Ⓑ Ⓒ Ⓓ

9. My grandparents have a few children and
                  A   B
   grandchildren. They love babys and young
                      C
   people.
    D

   Ⓐ Ⓑ Ⓒ Ⓓ

10. Clarissa doesn't usually like the
             A   B
    mushrooms, but she liked the mushrooms
                          C
    on the pizza at lunch.
        D

    Ⓐ Ⓑ Ⓒ Ⓓ

UNIT 5 PRONOUNS

5a Subject and Object Pronouns

Student Book p. 110

1 | Practice

Write *C* next to the sentence if the pronoun is correct. Write *I* if the pronoun is incorrect.

_____ 1. She's going to tell they the secret.

_____ 2. It's a secret.

_____ 3. We know it.

_____ 4. Her doesn't know it.

_____ 5. Him is wearing new shoes.

_____ 6. He gave us some directions.

_____ 7. Them weren't clear.

_____ 8. We got lost.

_____ 9. It was difficult to find.

_____ 10. I talked to he before we left.

_____ 11. He told I the way.

2 | Practice

Replace the underlined nouns with the subject and object pronouns.

1. Paul taught the students about the Gulf War.

   He taught them about it. _____.

2. Luanne studied law before Luanne married Robert.

   _____.

3. You and I are going to miss the bus.

   _____.

4. Don saw you and me at the party.

   _____.

5. Hannah drove Michael to the office.

   _____.

6. The directions weren't clear to Laura and Rob.

   _____.

Practice

Complete the sentences with subject or object pronouns.

A. Ted and Danielle wrote a report and

_____ put _____ on
　　　　1　　　　　　　　2

the desk. I called _____ because
　　　　　　　　　3

I didn't find _____. Someone
　　　　　　　　4

took _____. Ted and Danielle
　　　　5

wrote the report again. _____
　　　　　　　　　　　6

finished _____ at 4:00 and put _____ in a drawer. Then
　　　　　　7　　　　　　　　　　　　　8

_____ locked _____.
　　　9　　　　　　　　10

B. Jeremy is going to a new school, but he doesn't know anyone yet. _____
　　　　　　　　　　　　　　　　　　　　　　　　　　　　　1

decided to have a party, and yesterday _____ talked to some other students.
　　　　　　　　　　　　　　　　　2

Jeremy invited _____ to his apartment for the party. _____ came,
　　　　　　　　　3　　　　　　　　　　　　　　　4

and _____ had a good time.
　　　　5

C. Kate told the children a scary story, and now _____ are scared.
　　　　　　　　　　　　　　　　　　　　　1

_____ is really sorry she told _____ the story. _____ are
　　2　　　　　　　　　　　　　3　　　　　　　　　4

afraid to go to bed, and _____ feels bad.
　　　　　　　　　　5

D. Mother to daughter:

Mother: Have you cleaned your room today?

Daughter: Yes, Mom. I cleaned _____ an hour ago.
　　　　　　　　　　　　1

Mother: What about the dishes?

Daughter: I put _____ away. Can I call Lydia now?
　　　　　　　2

Mother: Not yet. _____ 're not finished. _____ need to make the
　　　　　　　　　3　　　　　　　　　　　4

bed. You can call _____ when _____ 're done.
　　　　　　　　5　　　　　　　6

5b Possessive Adjectives and Possessive Pronouns

Student Book p. 113

4 | Practice

Rewrite the sentences using both forms of the possessive pronouns. In some cases, only one choice may be possible.

1. It's <u>David's</u> toy.

   It's his toy. It's his.

2. They're not <u>Helen's</u> cigarettes.

   _____.

3. That's <u>my and my wife's</u> church.

   _____.

4. It's not <u>your turn</u>! It's <u>my turn</u>.

   _____.

5. That was my <u>grandparents'</u> business.

   _____.

6. Mom: Whose dirty dishes are these?
   Son: They're not <u>my dishes</u>.

   _____.

7. <u>Your mom</u> is a lot of fun.

   _____.

8. He's not <u>my and my husband's</u> cat.

   _____.

5 | Practice

Read the article about the blues. Then write the underlined possessive pronouns as possessive adjectives and the possessive adjectives as possessive pronouns.

Many people believe that blues music has its roots in Africa. Slaves sang <u>their songs</u> of
₁
loneliness, lost love, pain, and suffering and brought <u>their musical heritage</u> to North America.
₂
Some people believe blues music is a combination of African melody and western tones.

The blues became popular to white audiences when white singers based <u>their music</u> on the blues tradition. Elvis Presley sang "You Ain't
₃
Nothing But a Hound Dog," which Willie May "Big Mama" Thornton originally recorded in 1952. <u>Her version</u> is a little bit different from Elvis's.
₄

Some of the famous blues musicians from past and present are Muddy Waters, Bessie Smith, John Lee Hooker, Robert Johnson, to name only a few. Today, B.B. King is one of the most well-known blues guitarists to 20th century audiences. <u>His guitar</u>, Lucille, is
₅
almost as famous.

1. _____

2. _____

3. _____

4. _____

5. _____

5c Reflexive Pronouns

Student Book p. 115

6 Practice

Write *C* next to the sentence if the reflexive pronoun is correct. Write *I* if the reflexive pronoun is incorrect.

_____ **1.** He made it herself.

_____ **2.** We introduced ourselves.

_____ **3.** Jackie and John took care of it itself.

_____ **4.** I cut my hair by himself.

_____ **5.** You and Jean are going by yourselves.

_____ **6.** I just burned yourself on the pan.

_____ **7.** Rebecca didn't do her homework by herself.

_____ **8.** My friends and I enjoyed themselves.

_____ **9.** I taught myself how to sew.

_____ **10.** Michelle and Sarah are planning the conference themselves.

7 Practice

Complete the sentences with the correct reflexive pronoun.

1. Mother: What happened to the window?!

Son: I don't know.

Mother: Well, it didn't break _____!

2. My daughter and son-in-law are building

their own house and they're doing it

_____.

3. My best friend and I are planning to drive

across the country by _____ after

we graduate.

4. Kurt: I'm hungry.

Melissa: There's some tuna salad in the refrigerator. Help _____.

5. Marta and John: We're hungry.

   Todd: There's some pizza over there. Help _____.

6. George taught _____ how to play the guitar.

7. I'm doing this exercise by _____.

8. They started their own business because they wanted to work for _____.

9. Mother: Elizabeth! Dean! Stop fighting. If you don't behave _____,

   we're not going to the park.

10. Leroy: Ouch!

   Shanya: What happened?

   Leroy: I hurt _____.

11. Maria: What happened to Mr. Stevens?

   Sam: He cut _____ while he was shaving.

12. Vicky: Why are you talking to _____?

   Jim: I'm thinking out loud.

13. Giles: Who's that pretty girl over there?

   Charlie: That's my cousin, Susan. Go introduce _____.

14. Douglas: Why are you walking so slowly?

   Joyce: I hurt _____ while I was skiing.

15. Nick: Did Anna call the electrician yesterday?

   William: No, she fixed the problem _____.

16. Thanks for dinner. We really enjoyed _____.

17. Mandy: Wow, what's wrong with Ken? He looks terrible.

   Joe: I know. He isn't taking care of _____.

18. I hate cleaning the kitchen. I want a house that will clean _____.

19. Our cats clean _____.

20. Jay: What happened to the radio? Why did it stop?

   Amber: I don't know. It turned _____ off.

5d Another, The Other, Other, Others, and The Others

Student Book p. 118

8 Practice

Complete the sentences with *another* or *the other*.

1. Samantha: I need _____ pencil.

   Bob: Here. I have two. I'll keep one, and you can have _____.

2. Cesare: Would you like to dance?

   Betty: No, thanks. _____ time.

3. There are only three songs before the club closes. I think I'm going to dance to two

   of them and sit down for _____.

4. Renee: Would you like _____ piece of cake?

   Mel: Sure. It's delicious.

5. There are two slices of cake left. I'm going to have one. Would you like

   _____?

6. Ali has two sisters. One is in college and _____ is in high school.

7. Hey. There were four bottles of water, and now there are only two. What happened

   to _____ bottles?

8. Manicurist to customer:

   I finished with this hand. Please give me _____.

9. Karen had an eye test. First the doctor looked at one eye, and then

   _____.

10. Okay, here is the movie selection. There are three movies playing downtown. One is a

    scary movie, _____ is a romantic comedy, and _____ is a

    historical drama.

11. Kelly has two pairs of sunglasses, but one pair is broken, and she can't

    find _____.

12. Our family grows apples. Here, please take one. Have _____. We have a lot!

13. He took a step closer to me. Then, he took _____, and

    _____, and _____ until I told him to stop.

9 Practice

Write C next to the sentence if *other, the other, others,* or *the others* is used correctly. Write *I* if *other, the other, others,* or *the others* is used incorrectly.

_____ 1. I have some others ideas.

_____ 2. The others students aren't finished.

_____ 3. Other people are waiting to use the phone.

_____ 4. I work well with others.

_____ 5. I have a lot of friends. Some are men and the other are women.

10 Practice

Complete the sentences with *other, the other, others,* or *the others.*

1. Edward doesn't like college. Some classes are too easy, _____ are too difficult.

2. The museum is showing three styles right now. One is impressionism, another is abstract realism, and a third is surrealism. I like impressionism, but _____ don't interest me.

3. There are 13 students in my class. Seven of them are from Korea, four of them are from China, and _____ are from Japan.

4. Some TV shows are good, and _____ are not very funny.

5. My two favorite TV shows are on Sunday. One is on early, and _____ is on late.

6. The art teacher liked some of the pieces, but he said _____ pieces needed work.

11 Practice

Complete the sentences with *another, the other, others,* or *the others.*

A. One summer some friends of mine and I went on a backpacking trip. Two of us were women and _____ were men.
                                    1
_____ person wanted to come with us, but she couldn't. Three of us were
          2
from the United States, but _____ woman was from England originally.
                                    3
We went hiking for a month in the mountains.

My mom told me that some of the neighbors were worried about us; that it was dangerous for 19-year-olds to go so far away alone, but _____ thought it
4
was a great thing for us to do.

We had a wonderful time and we learned three important things. The first thing we learned was how to make group decisions. _____ thing we learned was how
5
to be independent, and _____ thing we learned was that everything we
6
needed we could carry on our backs.

B. One summer, my brother worked as a camp counselor in a summer camp. Some of the kids were from small towns, and _____ were from the city. He had five boys
1
in his cabin. One of them was a troublemaker, but _____ were very sweet.
2

The camp was on a lake, and my brother was a lifeguard. There were two of them. _____ lifeguard, John, was lazy. One time, John didn't see that one of the
3
boys was in trouble, and my brother jumped in the water to save him. _____
4
time, John didn't come to work all day, so my brother had to watch all the boys while they were swimming.

5e *One* and *Ones*
Student Book p. 121

|12| Practice
Complete the sentences with *one* or *ones*.

A. Anya: Which section are you in?

   Terry: The last _____, with Dr. Hardey.
1
   Anya: Did you buy your books?

   Terry: I bought the _____ on the list.
2
B. Steven: What do you think of the candy?

   Malcom: The black _____ are good, but I don't like the red _____.
1   2

C. Leslie: Which cars did you like?

Claudia: I liked the small, fast _____.

                                           1

Leslie: Which color car did you choose?

Claudia: I picked the dark green _____.

                                            2

Leslie: How about the stereo?

Claudia: I ordered the best _____.

                                            3

Leslie: Have you got the insurance?

Claudia: Not yet, but I'm thinking about the two basic _____.

                                                                   4

13   Practice

Complete the sentences with *one, ones, some, it,* or *them*.

1. I need a cup of coffee. Would you like _____, too?

2. Mike: Those pants are dirty.

   Patrick: I don't have any other _____.

3. Jessica: Let's go shopping for new pants.

   Ellen: Good idea. I need _____.

4. Those grapes look good. Let's get _____.

5. Paul: Have you got a computer for school? You'll need _____.

   Theresa: Yes, I have. I'm taking _____ with me tomorrow.

6. Paula: Which flowers do you like?

   Jeannie: I like the white _____.

7. Kirk: Here are your groceries.

   Vivian: Put _____ on the counter.

8. Rachel: I left my purse at the bank.

   Frank: Are you going to go get _____?

9. Are those mints? May I have _____?

10. I can't find my pen. Where is _____?

11. Katerina painted a few new paintings this year. I really like the _____ she just finished last week.

12. Gene: Here's your mail.

     Mei: Thanks. Could you put _____ on the table?

13. Sara: Did you look at apartments last weekend?

     Henri: Yes, the last _____ we looked at was okay.

14. Jody likes the new car, but I like the old _____ better.

5f Indefinite Pronouns

Student Book p. 123

14 Practice

Write *C* next to the sentence if the indefinite pronoun is correct. Write *I* if the indefinite pronoun is incorrect.

_____ **1.** He doesn't like anybody.

_____ **2.** There isn't nothing in the refrigerator.

_____ **3.** Everyone's coming tomorrow.

_____ **4.** Anyone is at the door.

_____ **5.** The children don't have anything to do.

_____ **6.** Nobody called while we were out.

_____ **7.** Yvonne isn't going nowhere.

_____ **8.** I called but someone didn't answer.

15 Practice

Underline the correct indefinite pronouns in parentheses.

1. Police officer 1:   What happened here?

    Police officer 2:   I don't know. There were a lot of people here, but

                                (no one / anyone) saw anything.

    Police officer 1:   Who did you question?

    Police officer 2:   I've asked (everyone / anyone) here.

2. Ngan: I don't remember where I parked my car. I can't find it, and I've looked

(somewhere / everywhere).

Seung: Okay, let's ask (anyone / someone) to help us.

3. Teacher: Why aren't you working?

Student: I don't have (nothing / anything) to do.

4. Max: What's wrong?

Dana: (Something / Everything). I hate my job, my car doesn't work, and

I never get to see my friends.

5. Hello? Is (anybody / nobody) home?

6. Carl: Are you okay?

Michael: No, I can't feel (something / anything) in my hand.

7. Doctor: How did you hurt yourself?

Bill: I'm not sure. I was working out, but I didn't do (everything / anything)

differently. (Something / Everything) is wrong, though. It hurts to walk.

8. Roommate 1:   I'm leaving. (Something / Nothing) you say will make me stay.

Roommate 2:   Why? I didn't do (anything / nothing) wrong!

9. Roommate 1:   I'm going to the store. Do you need (everything / anything)?

Roommate 2:   Nope. I have (everything / anything) I need.

10. Mom: You're late for school. (Everyone / Someone) is already on the bus.

Jennifer: I can't find my backpack (anywhere / nowhere).

A **Choose the best answer, A, B, C, or D, to complete the sentence. Mark your answer by darkening the oval with the same letter.**

1. These are _____.

   A. our   Ⓐ Ⓑ Ⓒ Ⓓ
   B. ours
   C. your
   D. their

2. Adrienne cut _____ on the knife.

   A. herself   Ⓐ Ⓑ Ⓒ Ⓓ
   B. ourselves
   C. themselves
   D. myself

3. _____ is wearing silver earrings.

   A. Hers   Ⓐ Ⓑ Ⓒ Ⓓ
   B. Her
   C. Anyone
   D. Everyone

4. Digital cameras are good, but old film _____ are better.

   A. one   Ⓐ Ⓑ Ⓒ Ⓓ
   B. the one
   C. ones
   D. another

5. Yum. This ice cream is good. Would you like _____ bowl?

   A. another   Ⓐ Ⓑ Ⓒ Ⓓ
   B. some
   C. it
   D. the other

6. The tea is in the kitchen. Please help _____.

   A. mine   Ⓐ Ⓑ Ⓒ Ⓓ
   B. theirs
   C. myself
   D. yourselves

7. My two sisters are older. One lives in Seattle, and _____ is in New York.

   A. another   Ⓐ Ⓑ Ⓒ Ⓓ
   B. some
   C. it
   D. the other

8. There were ten complaints. Four were about our sales people, three were about our prices, and _____ were about the product.

   A. another   Ⓐ Ⓑ Ⓒ Ⓓ
   B. some
   C. the others
   D. the other

9. Tara didn't see _____.

   A. someone   Ⓐ Ⓑ Ⓒ Ⓓ
   B. nobody
   C. nothing
   D. anyone

10. Whose watches are these? _____.

   A. Mine   Ⓐ Ⓑ Ⓒ Ⓓ
   B. My
   C. Hers watches
   D. Her

B **Find the underlined word or phrase, A, B, C, or D, that is incorrect. Mark your answer by darkening the oval with the same letter.**

1. I'm not sure if he is going to come, but
   A   B
   she sister is going to come.
   C   D

   Ⓐ Ⓑ Ⓒ Ⓓ

2. Javier and Kimberley have a car.
   A   B
   The blue one is their.
   C   D

   Ⓐ Ⓑ Ⓒ Ⓓ

3. Jack built his company by yourself.
   A   B
   Nobody helped him.
   C   D

   Ⓐ Ⓑ Ⓒ Ⓓ

4. Anyone took the bananas. I only ate one
   A   B   C
   and the others were on the counter.
   D

   Ⓐ Ⓑ Ⓒ Ⓓ

5. I looked anywhere. Someone took
   A   B
   my keys. They were on the dining room
   C   D
   table.

   Ⓐ Ⓑ Ⓒ Ⓓ

6. Let's get some tomatoes. Ones over there
   A   B   C
   look good.
   D

   Ⓐ Ⓑ Ⓒ Ⓓ

7. It's not your bag, it's my. Yours is on
   A   B   C   D
   the floor.

   Ⓐ Ⓑ Ⓒ Ⓓ

8. Which lotion do you like? This one or
   A   B   C
   that ones?
   D

   Ⓐ Ⓑ Ⓒ Ⓓ

9. Terrel made it by himself. Anyone
   A   B   C
   helped him.
   D

   Ⓐ Ⓑ Ⓒ Ⓓ

10. The glasses are theirs, but the dishes
    A   B   C
    are our.
    D

    Ⓐ Ⓑ Ⓒ Ⓓ

UNIT 6 THE PERFECT TENSES

6a The Present Perfect Tense
Student Book p. 130

1 **Practice**

Complete the following chart. Use the simple present tense, the simple past tense, and the past participle of the verbs.

Verb	Simple Present Tense	Simple Past Tense	Past Participle
1. be	is, am, are		
2.		ate	
3.			given
4. drink			
5.			gotten
6.		had	
7.		knew	
8. put			
9.		read	
10.			seen
11.		took	
12. write			

2 **Practice**

Complete the sentences with the present perfect tense of the verbs in parentheses. Then complete the questions and write answers.

A. Tom: I am so lazy today. I have so much to

do, and I (not, do) _____
                                  1
much. I (not, make) _____
                                  2
the bed, and I (not, take)_____
                                  3
out the garbage. I (not, call) _____
                                  4
my professor or (finish) _____
                                  5
my paper yet, and it's already 3:00 P.M.!

a. (call) _____ Tom _____ his professor yet?

b. _____ .

c. (get) _____ Tom _____ dressed yet?

d. _____ .

e. What (do) _____ Tom _____ today?

f. _____ .

B.   Interviewer: Tell me about your work experience. What (do) _____ you
1

_____?
(1)

Lewis: Well, I (study) _____ three languages and (travel)
2

_____ around the world. I (be) _____ to
3 4

Moscow twice. I (work) _____ on many sales teams, and I
5

(have) _____ a lot of experience working with people.
6

a. (be) _____ he _____ a waiter?

b. _____ .

c. (travel) _____ he _____ a lot?

d. _____ .

e. What other experience (have) _____ he _____?

f. _____ .

C.   Monique: (finish) _____ you _____ the assignment?
1 (1)

Scott: Yes, I (have) _____. I (not, sleep) _____ for two
2 3

nights, but it's finally done! What about you? (finish) _____
4

you _____ it?
(4)

Monique: No, I (not, have) _____.
5

a. (finish) _____ Scott _____ the assignment?

b. _____ .

c. (finish) _____ Monique _____ the assignment?

d. _____ .

D. Terry had a very different life 10 years ago. He ate too much, was single, watched a lot of TV, and didn't have any friends. He was very unhappy. He quit overeating 10 years ago, and he (not, watch) _____ too much TV in 10 years.

1
He (start) _____ exercising, and he (make) _____ new friends.

2   3
He (be) _____ married to his second wife for seven years. His children

4
(become) _____ closer to him. He (change) _____ his life

5   6
dramatically, and today, Terry is a very happy man.

a. (stop) _____ Terry _____ overeating?

b. _____ .

c. (be) _____ he _____ single for seven years?

d. _____ .

e. What (happen) _____ to Terry and his children?

f. _____ .

g. (change) _____ he _____ his life?

h. _____ .

6b *For* and *Since*

Student Book p. 136

3   Practice

Write *for* or *since* for the following phrases.

_____ **a.** my last vacation

_____ **b.** three months

_____ **c.** 50 years

_____ **d.** last week

_____ **e.** ten minutes

_____ **f.** 10:00 A.M.

_____ **g.** I graduated from college

_____ **h.** Saturday night

_____ **i.** this morning

_____ **j.** a few days

_____ **k.** half a day

_____ **l.** 2000

_____ **m.** a long time

_____ **n.** last night

_____ **o.** Tuesday

_____ **p.** we started this exercise

_____ **q.** a year

_____ **r.** seven days

_____ **s.** breakfast

4 | Practice

Write C next to the sentence if *for* or *since* is used correctly. Write I if *for* or *since* is used incorrectly.

_____ **1.** Kathy's worked in the hotel since 1998.

_____ **2.** Todd's had a headache for 1:00.

_____ **3.** Jeannie's been a teacher for eight years.

_____ **4.** Karl hasn't smoked since a year.

_____ **5.** Brian's had long hair for nine years.

_____ **6.** They've lived in Singapore since 2001.

_____ **7.** I haven't seen you since my last birthday!

_____ **8.** Laurel hasn't seen her cousins for last year.

_____ **9.** Choi hasn't been to Korea since he was 20 years old.

_____ **10.** Donna and her parents haven't seen each other for Tuesday.

5 Practice

Complete the sentences about you, your parents, and your friends.

1. I _____ since this morning.

2. I _____ for 24 hours.

3. I _____ since _____.

4. I (not) _____ for _____.

5. My parents _____ since _____.

6. My friend(s) _____ for _____.

7. My English class _____ since _____.

6c Ever and Never

Student Book p. 138

6 Practice

Write C next to the sentence if *ever* or *never* is used correctly. Write I if *ever* or *never* is used incorrectly.

_____ 1. We've ever seen that movie.

_____ 2. Jana's never been married.

_____ 3. Have the Washingtons ever been to Toronto?

_____ 4. No, they never have.

_____ 5. Elaine's ever met the neighbors.

7 Practice

Write questions and answers using the prompts.

1. ever/be in a car accident

   Have you ever been in a car accident?

   Yes, I have, but I was okay.

2. ever/do military service

   _____ ?

   No, _____ , but I will next year.

3. ever/break a leg

_____?

No, _____, but I've broken my arm.

4. ever/live in a dormitory

_____?

Yes, _____. I lived in one my first year at college.

5. ever/play basketball

_____?

Yes, _____. I just played yesterday!

6. ever/grow a beard

_____?

No, _____. I'm a woman!

7. ever/study calculus

_____?

No, _____. I wasn't very good at math in school.

8. ever/swim in the ocean

_____?

No, _____. I don't know how to swim.

9. ever/break a mirror

_____?

Yes, _____. I dropped it while I was moving.

10. ever/use a typewriter

_____?

No, _____. What's a

typewriter?

8 Practice

Write questions and answers about yourself with *have you ever* and the prompts.

1. get a driver's license

   Have you ever gotten a driver's license?

   No, I haven't.

2. bake a cake

   _____?

   _____.

3. go to another country

   _____?

   _____.

4. speak English in the United States

   _____?

   _____.

5. study the present perfect before

   _____?

   _____.

6. have a pet

   _____?

   _____.

7. order a pizza

   _____?

   _____.

8. buy a house

   _____?

   _____.

9. go surfing

   _____?

   _____.

10. wear makeup

_____?

_____.

11. pierce your nose or eyebrow

_____?

_____.

12. do magic tricks

_____?

_____.

6d *Already, Yet,* and *Just*

Student Book p. 140

9 | Practice

Underline the correct words in parentheses.

1. Has she arrived (just / yet)?

2. Yes, she's (just / yet) gotten here.

3. We've (already / yet) eaten. Are you hungry?

4. Yes, I am. I haven't eaten (already / yet).

5. Steve hasn't called you (just / yet)?

6. He's (just / yet) sent you email.

7. The children haven't seen the pirate movie (just / yet).

8. My kids have (already / yet) seen it.

9. Have you gone to the dentist (yet / just)?

10. No, not (just / yet).

10 **Practice**

Write sentences using the present perfect with *already* or *yet* and the prompts.

1. invent flying cars

   People haven't invented flying cars yet .

2. discover radio waves

   _____ .

3. find cure for colds

   _____ .

4. build cities on the moon

   _____ .

5. discover electricity

   _____ .

6. make robots

   _____ .

7. find answer to world hunger

   _____ .

8. make airplanes

   _____ .

9. (your choice)

   _____ .

10. (your choice)

    _____ .

11 Practice

When Belinda was 10 years old, she made a list of things she wanted to do in her life. She's already done some of them, but she hasn't done others yet. Read the list and write sentences using the present perfect and *already* or *yet*.

Things I want to do
1. finish college ✔
2. find a good job
3. see the pyramids in Egypt
4. see the Great Wall of China ✔
5. parachute out of an airplane ✔
6. climb Mt. Everest
7. move to California ✔
8. become a famous singer

1. *She has already finished college*   .

2. _____ .

3. _____ .

4. _____ .

5. _____ .

6. _____ .

7. _____ .

8. _____ .

12 Practice

Write five goals you had for your life when you were 10 years old.

Example: *When I was 10, I wanted to study ballet.*

1. _____ .

2. _____ .

3. _____ .

4. _____ .

5. _____ .

Read your list and write sentences using the present perfect and *already* or *yet*.

Example: ___*I haven't studied ballet yet.*___

1. _____ .

2. _____ .

3. _____ .

4. _____ .

5. _____ .

6e The Simple Past Tense OR the Present Perfect Tense

Student Book p. 142

13 Practice

Read the sentences. Write *P* next to the sentence if the action is in the past or is finished. Write *N* (for *now*) if the action is still true in the present.

_____ 1. They got married two weeks ago.

_____ 2. I didn't go to the wedding.

_____ 3. Have they come back from their honeymoon?

_____ 4. No, they've been in Fiji for two weeks.

_____ 5. I've already gotten a postcard from them.

_____ 6. I got it two days ago.

_____ 7. Her parents haven't heard from them yet.

_____ 8. They've known each other since they were in high school.

_____ 9. The wedding was beautiful.

_____ 10. I haven't bought them a present yet.

14 Practice

Read the sentences. Then write a sentence using the present perfect tense.

1. Three years ago, Cindy bought a new truck. She still has her truck today.

   ___*She's had her truck for three years*_____ .

2. Serena and Jacob arrived in Canada in 1998. They're still there.

   _____ .

3. Jim got his dog in February. He still has him.

_____.

4. Jan stopped smoking six years ago. She still doesn't smoke.

_____.

5. My country became independent in 1978. It's still independent.

_____.

6. The movie started at 7:00. We're still in the theater.

_____.

7. Kevin's best friend and Kevin had an argument three months ago. They still don't talk to each other.

_____.

8. Mona dyed her hair for the first time a few years ago. She still dyes her hair.

_____.

9. Matthew got depressed after his mother died. He's still depressed today.

_____.

10. Jocelyn started piano lessons when she was 10 years old. She still plays piano today.

_____.

15 Practice

Complete the sentences with the simple past or present perfect of the verbs in parentheses.

A. Alan: (buy) _____ you _____ tickets yet?
                          1   (1)

P.J.: Yes, I _____ . I (get) _____ them last night. I
                     2   3

(be) _____ lucky. I (get) _____ the last two tickets.
            4   5

Alan: (pay) _____ I _____ you yet?
                    6   (6)

P.J.: No, you _____ .
                       7

B. Vicky: (see) _____ you _____ the office?
                            1   (1)

Shelly: No, I _____ . Why?
                       2

Vicky: Someone (paint) _____ it bright yellow over the weekend!
                                      3

Shelly: Oh, no!

C. Teacher: Please hand in your assignment.

Student: I (not, finish) _____ yet.
                                1

Teacher: Why not?

Student: My computer (crash) _____ last night.
                                        2

D. Judy: (stop) _____ it _____ raining?
                    1   (1)

Peter: Yes, it _____. It (stop) _____ about an hour ago.
                    2   3

E. Antonio: Are you hungry? (eat) _____ you _____?
                                            1   (1)

Serena: Yes, I _____. Thanks anyway.
                    2

F. Jae: This looks like a nice restaurant.

Isabella: It is. I (eat) _____ here before.
                                1

Jae: Oh, when?

Isabella: I (be) _____ here about a year ago.
                        2

Jae: (be) _____ the food good?
                3

Isabella: Yes, it _____.
                        4

G. Jon: Ouch, my tooth really hurts!

Celine: (call) _____ you _____ the dentist yet?
                    1   (1)

Jon: Yes, I (call) _____ a little while ago, and I (make)
                            2

_____ an appointment.
            3

H. Sean: How long (work) _____ he _____ here?
                                    1   (1)

Keenan: I think he (be) _____ here for a long time.
                                2

Sean: When (start) _____ he _____?
                            3   (3)

Keenan: I think he (come) _____ here about 12 years ago.
                                    4

| 16 | Practice |

Read the following questions about your country and/or city. Answer them using the present perfect and _for, since, never,_ or _always._

1. Is your country independent?

Yes, my country has been independent since 1965. (OR)

My country has always been independent. (OR)

My country has never had independence.

2. Does your country compete in the World Cup?

_____.

3. Does your country use nuclear power?

_____.

4. Do women make as much money as men in your country?

_____.

5. Are there no-smoking sections in restaurants in your city?

_____.

6. Do men do military service in your country?

_____.

6f The Present Perfect Progressive Tense

Student Book p. 144

[17] Practice

Complete the sentences with the present perfect progressive of the verbs in parentheses.

1. Jessica: What (do) _____ you _____?

Your teeth are blue!

Michael: I (chew) _____ some bubble gum.

2. Receptionist: Oh, I didn't see you! How long (sit) _____ you

_____ there?

Kate: I (wait) _____ for 90 minutes.

3. This is Janice's favorite painting. She (work) _____

on it for eight months.

4. My friend's mom (make) _____ jam for over 30 years.

5. Carole: What are you thinking about?

Tom: Lunch.

Carole: How long (think) _____ you _____ about lunch?

Tom: All morning. My stomach (growl) _____ since 10:00!

6. She (cry) _____ since she heard the bad news.

7. Terry: Hi, how are you? What (do) _____ you _____?

   Cindy: I (work) _____ a lot, and I (teach) _____

   a night class. I (also, go) _____ to a yoga class.

8. Traffic is really bad. We (sit) _____ here for 20 minutes.

   Maureen (get) _____ worried she's going to be late for work.

9. Linda: Wow, it's quiet.

   Craig: Yes, the kids (sleep) _____ for almost two hours.

10. Nicole and Doug (attend) _____ college since they finished high school.

11. So many things (happen) _____ since we last saw you! Max (learn)

    _____ how to snowboard. The baby (walk) _____ a lot.

    Larry (make) _____ more money, and I (lose) _____

    weight.

12. My wife and I (think) _____ about moving. We (have)

    _____ trouble with our neighbors, so we (think) _____

about buying a new house.

18 Practice

Read the following information. Write a sentence using the present perfect progressive tense.

1. Greg started watching TV three hours ago. He's still watching TV now.

   Greg's been watching TV for three hours _____.

2. Chandra started smoking when she was 17 years old. She still smokes now.

   _____.

3. Jill got on the phone after she came home. She's still talking on the phone now.

   _____.

4. Shawna started taking vitamins a year ago. She still takes them now.

   _____.

5. Bob got a job delivering pizzas nine months ago. He still delivers them now.

   _____.

6. Carlos started shopping at 9:00 this morning, and he's still shopping now.

_____.

7. The boys started playing video games when they got home from school. They're still playing games now.

_____.

8. Gus started yawning about 20 minutes ago. He's yawning right now.

_____.

6g The Present Perfect Tense OR the Present Perfect Progressive Tense

Student Book p. 146

19 Practice

Read the sentences. Write *P* next to the sentence if the action is in the past or is finished. Write *N* (for *now*) if the action is still happening in the present.

_____ **1.** The class has finished the assignment.

_____ **2.** My friends' class has been working on it for 30 minutes.

_____ **3.** Kenji's gone home.

_____ **4.** Mary and Susan have been traveling for 10 days.

_____ **5.** Reuben's eaten dinner.

_____ **6.** The children have been eating dinner for half an hour.

_____ **7.** Elisa's been working since she was 14 years old.

_____ **8.** Susan's worked in construction.

_____ **9.** My daughter's gone to sleep.

_____ **10.** My dad's been wearing the same coat for 15 years!

20 Practice

Complete the sentences with the present perfect or the present perfect progressive of the verbs in parentheses. More than one answer may be possible.

A. Arnold: They (build) _____ that apartment complex for 18

                          1

               months. Why (take) _____ it _____ so long?

                                 2   (2)

    Maria: They (have) _____ a few problems. The city

                                3

(not, give) _____ the owners permission to put in a

4
pool, and they (change) _____ architects twice.

5
The builders also (not, receive) _____ all the

6
materials they need.

B. Martha: What's the matter?

    Joe: I (sit) _____ at my computer all day, and I

1
(not, finish) _____ my project yet.

2

    Martha: Why?

    Joe: Well, it (crash) _____ a couple times, and the printer

3
(not, work) _____ since I installed it.

4

C. Boss: What (do) _____ you _____? I

1   (1)
(wait) _____ for your report for an hour.

2

    Employee: I (talk) _____ with the team, and we

3
(make) _____ notes.

4

D. Sylvia: How long (work) _____ you _____ here?

1   (1)

    Lauren: I (work) _____ here for about six months, but I

2
(cut) _____ hair for 13 years. I really like this salon.

3
I (learn) _____ some new

4
techniques from my coworkers.

E. Anya (start) _____ working out, and

1
she feels great. She (stop) _____ going

2
to the aerobics class, but she (do) _____

3
yoga for a long time. She (try) _____ a few

4
other classes, but she likes yoga the best. She (practice)

_____ yoga for three years.

5

F. Daphne is an English teacher. Since September, Daphne

(work) _____ with young adults, and she (teach)

1

_____ other young teachers how to teach. She (have)

2

_____ a lot of experience in her field. She (learn)

3

_____ a lot from her students, and she (visit)

4

_____ many places around the world. She (study)

5

_____ Japanese and Spanish.

6

G. The city government (try) _____ to change some social

1

problems. They (already, provide) _____ 600 new jobs

2

and (give) _____ money to educational programs. They (work)

3

_____ on a theater program for teenagers from low-income

4

homes for a couple weeks.

21 **Practice**

Read the following information. Write a sentence using the present perfect progressive or present perfect tense. More than one answer may be possible.

1. Adam saw that movie two weeks ago, last week, and again last night.

_He's seen that movie three times_____.

2. Andy took off his glasses last night. He's not wearing them now.

_He hasn't been wearing his glasses since last night_____.

3. The LeGrands moved here in 1990. They still live here now.

_____.

4. Chris lay down in bed at 2:00. He's still lying there now.

_____.

5. Dori and Roberto got married in 2002. They're still married now.

_____.

6. Donny went to Italy in 1999. He went again in 2003.

_____.

7. We sent him email at 8:30 and again at midnight.

_____.

6h The Past Perfect Tense

Student Book p. 149

22 **Practice**

Complete the sentences using the past perfect or the simple past tense.

1. She (already, close) _____ the car door when she (see)

    _____ that she (leave) _____ her keys inside.

2. When the baby (start) _____ to cry, Eileen and Mike (just, fall)

    _____ asleep.

3. Rachel (be) _____ absent a week before she (tell) _____ her teachers.

4. Ing Chul (already, leave) _____ when Javier (come) _____

    looking for her.

5. When the police (arrive) _____, the thieves (leave) _____.

6. The politician (be) _____ an actor before he (become) _____

    involved in politics.

7. When their daughter (decide) _____ to take music lessons, her parents

    (already, sell) _____ their piano.

8. My wife and I (not, finish) _____ watching the movie when

    someone in front of us (shout) _____ out the ending.

9. Luckily, Miriam and Janet (get) _____ to the dock before the ship

    (leave) _____.

10. The frantic mother (already, call) _____ 911 when her son

    (walk) _____ in the door.

23 **Practice**

Read each pair of sentences. Decide which action happened first and which happened second. Combine them into sentences using the past perfect or the simple past tense.

1. The car broke down. It started to rain.

    _It had started to rain when the car broke down_____.

2. We left. He called.

    _____.

3. We didn't go very far. The car broke down.

_____.

4. We realized we left the cell phone in the trunk. We looked for the cell phone.

_____.

5. We were in the car for two hours. The tow truck arrived.

_____.

6. We got home. We realized we had lost the keys, so we slept in the car.

_____.

24 Practice

Answer the questions using the past perfect tense.

1. Why did the company go out of business?

One of the managers had stolen a lot of money .

2. Why didn't she eat lunch?

_____.

3. Why didn't you answer the phone last night?

_____.

4. Why was your roommate angry when you brought home a pizza last night?

_____.

5. Why did Mr. McClean get the job in Australia?

_____.

6. Why did the sales team have to redo their project?

_____.

7. Why did Kelly get that reward?

_____.

8. Why did the Browns adopt the two children?

_____.

25 Practice

Complete the sentences with your own ideas. Use the present progressive or the simple past tense.

1. _____ when the phone rang.

2. They'd already put out the fire when _____.

3. Vince and Cheryl _____ when we visited them in France.

4. I hadn't seen Luanne in a long time before _____.

5. When we got married, _____.

6i The Past Perfect Progressive Tense

Student Book p. 153

26 Practice

Read the sentences. Write *P* next to the sentence if the action is in the past or is finished. Write *N* (for *now*) if the action is still in progress in the present.

_____ 1. Our neighbors have been traveling for two weeks now.

_____ 2. They'd been working very hard.

_____ 3. The software company has been growing quickly.

_____ 4. It had been producing 1,000 units a day.

_____ 5. My grandparents have already eaten.

_____ 6. They ate at 7:00 this morning.

_____ 7. Mr. Leier has been teaching art history for a long time.

_____ 8. The Lees have been married for 30 years.

_____ 9. Michelle hadn't been working for her family's business for very long.

_____ 10. She'd found another job.

27 Practice

Complete the sentences using the past perfect progressive or the simple past of the verbs in parentheses.

1. They (work) _____ for five days before they

   (hear) _____ that the project (cancel) _____.

2. Before she finally (leave) _____, she (wait) _____

   for 45 minutes for him to arrive.

3. Wayne (wear) _____ the same boots for 15 years before his

   son (throw) _____ them away.

4. When it (start) _____ to rain, Min (wash) _____

   his car for 45 minutes.

5. The two sides (fight) _____ for a while before they (learn)

   _____ the war (be) _____ over.

6. My aunt (live) _____ in Australia for 10 years before she (see)

   _____ a koala bear.

7. Before the owner finally (turn) _____ it off, the car alarm (go)

   _____ off for 30 minutes.

8. When the earthquake (hit) _____, we (not, sit)

   _____ in the restaurant very long.

9. When you (call) _____ me, I (just, think) _____

   about you!

10. The team (have) _____ a good time when the accident

    (happen) _____.

28 | Practice

Complete the sentences with the simple past or the past perfect progressive.

1. I'd been doing this exercise for _____ when

   _____.

2. Last night I'd been sleeping for _____

   when _____.

3. My parents _____ before I left for school yesterday.

4. When _____, my best friend _____.

5. Before _____, my grandmother _____.

A **Choose the best answer, A, B, C, or D, to complete the sentence. Mark your answer by darkening the oval with the same letter.**

1. Fran and Charles _____ each other in four years.

   A. didn't see   Ⓐ Ⓑ Ⓒ Ⓓ
   B. haven't seen
   C. haven't been seeing
   D. seen

2. We've been here _____ an hour.

   A. since   Ⓐ Ⓑ Ⓒ Ⓓ
   B. already
   C. yet
   D. for

3. Hetty's _____ taken the photographs.

   A. since   Ⓐ Ⓑ Ⓒ Ⓓ
   B. already
   C. yet
   D. for

4. My grandfather hasn't made dinner _____.

   A. since   Ⓐ Ⓑ Ⓒ Ⓓ
   B. already
   C. yet
   D. for

5. They _____ many problems with the new telephone system.

   A. 've had   Ⓐ Ⓑ Ⓒ Ⓓ
   B. had been
   C. has had
   D. has been having

6. Her hands were sore because she _____ for four hours.

   A. has been typing   Ⓐ Ⓑ Ⓒ Ⓓ
   B. has typed
   C. had been typing
   D. have been typing

7. Before the bus arrived, Brian and Kumiko _____ talking.

   A. has finished   Ⓐ Ⓑ Ⓒ Ⓓ
   B. have finished
   C. hasn't finished
   D. had finished

8. He _____ divorced before he met his second wife.

   A. has been   Ⓐ Ⓑ Ⓒ Ⓓ
   B. had been
   C. has been divorcing
   D. have been

9. Hiroyuki and Thomas _____ since last night. They are almost finished.

   A. have   Ⓐ Ⓑ Ⓒ Ⓓ
   B. have worked
   C. worked
   D. have been working

10. Ray's _____ done the washing.

    A. since   Ⓐ Ⓑ Ⓒ Ⓓ
    B. already
    C. yet
    D. for

B Find the underlined word or phrase, A, B, C, or D, that is incorrect. Mark your answer by darkening the oval with the same letter.

1. Dr. Randy <u>has</u> <u>been</u> a dentist <u>since</u>
           A   B   C

   12 years. He'<u>s been working</u> in San
                D

   Francisco for a long time.

2. His son had <u>already</u> <u>brush</u> his teeth <u>when</u>
               A   B   C

   I <u>made</u> some hot chocolate.
     D

   Ⓐ Ⓑ Ⓒ Ⓓ

3. The owners <u>have</u> <u>knew</u> about the problem
              A   B

   with the roof <u>since</u> <u>the winter</u>.
               C   D

   Ⓐ Ⓑ Ⓒ Ⓓ

4. Ed has <u>yet</u> <u>gone</u> to bed. He's been
          A   B

   <u>sleeping</u> <u>for</u> a couple hours.
    C   D

   Ⓐ Ⓑ Ⓒ Ⓓ

5. Some of the students <u>didn't</u> <u>felt</u>
                  A   B

   well <u>since</u> they <u>ate</u> breakfast.
        C   D

   Ⓐ Ⓑ Ⓒ Ⓓ

6. The author <u>has</u> <u>already</u> finished college
             A   B

   <u>before</u> he <u>wrote</u> his first book.
    C   D

   Ⓐ Ⓑ Ⓒ Ⓓ

7. He'<u>s come</u> home <u>yet</u>. He'<u>d called</u> before
     A   B   C

   he <u>left</u> the office.
     D

   Ⓐ Ⓑ Ⓒ Ⓓ

8. The company <u>had</u> <u>decide</u> to give Monique
              A   B

   a better position when <u>she</u> <u>found</u> a new
                   C   D

   job.

   Ⓐ Ⓑ Ⓒ Ⓓ

9. It's <u>been</u> <u>snowing</u> <u>for</u> the morning. I've
       A   B   C

   <u>gone</u> outside three times.
    D

   Ⓐ Ⓑ Ⓒ Ⓓ

10. The team has <u>been winning</u> the
               A

    championship <u>three times</u>. They
               B

    <u>hadn't won</u> a game <u>before</u> 1999.
     C   D

    Ⓐ Ⓑ Ⓒ Ⓓ

UNIT 7 QUESTIONS AND PHRASAL VERBS

7a Yes/No Questions and Short Answers
Student Book p. 160

1 Practice

Following is an interview with a retired international sales manager. Answer the questions.

1. Do you have a few minutes to talk?

   Yes, _____ I do _____.

2. Are you still an international sales manager?

   No, _____.

3. Were you a marketing manager for your company?

   No, _____. I was always in sales.

4. Did you travel a lot?

   Yes, _____.

5. Did you work only in Europe?

   No, _____.

6. Have you been to Korea?

   Yes, _____. I've been there many times. I met my husband there.

7. Is your husband Korean?

   Yes, _____.

8. Does he work?

   Yes, _____. He's a stockbroker.

9. Can you speak Korean now?

   Yes, _____.

10. Are you thinking of returning to sales?

    No, _____.

11. Should we take a break now?

    Yes, _____.

Practice

Read the questions and write answers to them.

1. Are there five colors in a rainbow?

   _____.

2. Can giraffes fly?

   _____.

3. Had people used phones before they used email?

   _____.

4. Have doctors discovered a cure for AIDS?

   _____.

5. Was Lady Diana Spencer from Germany?

   _____.

6. Could women vote 20 years ago in the United States?

   _____.

7. Was Beethoven from El Salvador?

   _____.

8. Should people speed up at red lights?

   _____.

9. Does popcorn grow on trees?

   _____.

10. It is usually warm in Florida?

    _____.

11. Do we use keys in locks?

    _____.

12. Will people live on other planets in the future?

    _____.

3 Practice

Answer the questions about yourself.

1. Do you like English? _____.

2. Can you play the guitar? _____.

3. Must we help other people? _____.

4. Should we study other cultures? _____.

5. Must all students attend college? _____.

6. Would you like some tea now? _____.

7. Are you a happy person? _____.

8. Do you smoke? _____.

9. Could you do cartwheels when you were younger? _____.

10. Can you do cartwheels now? _____.

11. Is your mom a good cook? _____.

12. Is your dad a good cook? _____.

13. Have you ever been in a car accident? _____.

4 Practice

Write questions about yourself based on the answers.

1. _Will you be home tonight_ _____?

   No, I won't.

2. _____?

   Yes, I have.

3. _____?

   No, we couldn't.

4. _____?

   No, they didn't.

5. _____?

   No, I don't have to.

7b Questions with Wh- Words

Student Book p. 163

5 Practice

Match the questions with the answers about the Taj Mahal.

_____ **1.** How many workers built it?

_____ **2.** Who built it?

_____ **3.** When did his wife die?

_____ **4.** Is the Taj Mahal in Afghanistan?

_____ **5.** Did it take 22 years to build?

a. Yes, it did.

b. 1631.

c. No, it isn't.

d. About 20,000.

e. Shah Jahan.

6 Practice

Write questions based on the answers about the ancient African city of Timbuktu.

1. _____ ?

It's in Mali, near the Niger River. (where)

2. _____ ?

It was invaded by Morocco in 1593. (who)

3. _____ ?

It was famous for gold trade. (what)

4. _____ ?

In the 15th and 16th centuries it was a famous educational center. (when)

5. _____

_____ ?

There was a university and about 100 schools for the Koran. (what)

6. _____

_____ ?

Today it's an important meeting center for people in the Sahara. (why)

7 Practice

Write questions based on the answers about emperor penguins.

1. _What are emperor penguins?_

   Emperor penguins are <u>the biggest penguins in the penguin family</u>. (what)

2. _____?

   They are sometimes almost half the size of an adult human and <u>can weigh up to about 65 pounds</u>. (how much)

3. _____?

   They live on the <u>continent of Antarctica</u>. (where)

4. _____?

   They are <u>black and have yellow and white feathers near the neck</u>. (what)

5. _____?

   The female lays <u>one egg a year</u> and then leaves the egg with the father while she goes off to sea. (how many)

6. _____?

   _____?

   <u>The male</u> keeps the egg warm on his feet and covers it with his stomach for 65 days, in <u>the middle of winter</u>! (who) (when)

7. _____?

   When the baby hatches, the male feeds it <u>until the female returns</u>. Then it's his turn to go look for food. (how long)

7c Questions with *Who* and *What* as the Subject
Student Book p. 166

8 Practice

Read the story about a surprise party. Then ask and answer the questions with *who* or *what*.

Emily and Kyle went to a surprise party for their next-door neighbor, Roberto, but it was a disaster! Roberto's wife, Maria, was nervous and busy. Maria had invited all Roberto's friends, but not many people came. Roberto's mother, Mrs. Garcia, was there, but she wasn't happy. Mrs. Garcia told Maria that Maria hadn't prepared enough food and that her house wasn't clean enough. Then Maria and Roberto's dog, Marko, ate the birthday cake. Finally, Roberto came home, but he had a cold and didn't feel well.

1. _____ went to the surprise party?

_____.

2. _____ was nervous and busy?

_____.

3. _____ is Mrs. Garcia?

_____.

4. _____ did Mrs. Garcia tell her daughter-in-law?

_____.

5. _____ happened to the birthday cake?

_____.

6. _____ was sick?

_____.

9 Practice

Read the story about a fight. Then ask and answer the questions with *who* or *what*.

Bruno woke up suddenly at 3:30 in the morning. His neighbors were screaming very loudly. He heard a crash. He called the police. The police arrived and talked to Bruno's neighbors, Ed Bronson and Emily Craig. Mr. Bronson told the police that he had tripped over a rug and fallen. He had cut his forehead and broken his arm.

1. _____ heard the screaming?

_____.

2. _____ did he hear?

_____.

3. _____ called the police?

_____.

4. _____ did he say?

_____.

5. _____ was hurt?

_____.

6. _____ happened?

_____.

7. _____did Mr. Bronson fall over?

_____.

⑩ Practice

Complete the sentences with *who* or *what*.

A. Someone knocking at a door:

Jim: _____ 's there?

1

Sarah: It's me.

Jim: _____ do you want?

2

Sarah: May I use your phone?

B. Hakim, a businessman, missed his flight because he didn't have the right flight number or time. Now he's at the airport talking to his office.

Tom: _____ happened?

1

Hakim: I missed my plane. _____ made the plans? _____

2 3

bought this ticket?

Tom: Our Los Angles office. I'll call them right now. _____ are you

4

going to do?

Hakim: I'll try to get another flight.

C. Young: _____ was at the party?

1

Choi: Irene, Kevin, Sachiko, Nikki, and David.

Young: _____ did you do?

2

Choi: We talked and ate some snacks. Then we went out. _____ did

3

you do?

Young: Nothing.

7d Questions with *Which* and *What*

Student Book p. 168

1 Practice

Complete the sentences with *which* or *what*.

A. Nancy: _____ is your major?
        1

James: Chemistry.

Nancy: That's mine, too. _____ classes are you taking?
                         2

James: Intro to chemistry and some general education classes.

Nancy: _____ teacher do you have, Dr. Fredrick or Dr. Saunders?
        3

James: I have Saunders.

Nancy: _____ book are you using, *Fundamentals* or *General Introduction*?
        4

James: We're using a new book this semester, but I forget the name.

B. Peggy: _____ suitcase are you taking, the small black one or the old
        1
        cloth one?

Duncan: I think I'll take the black one. _____ tie looks better, the blue
                                          2
        one or the red one?

Peggy: I like the red one. Do you know _____ suit you're going to
                                        3
        wear for the interview?

Duncan: I think the dark gray one.

C. Jun: _____ 's your favorite food?
        1
Beth: I love Italian food.

Jun: _____ restaurant is your favorite?
      2
Beth: I really like Lorenzo's on Main Street.

Jun: _____ do you usually order?
      3
Beth: I usually get the linguini and clams.

D. Chie: _____'s your favorite holiday?

　　　　　　1

Doug: I love New Year's.

Chie: _____ do you usually do?

　　　　　　2

Doug: We visit our cousins.

Chie: _____ cousins? The ones near you or the ones across town?

　　　　　　3

Doug: We see both.

Chie: _____ do you eat?

　　　　　　4

Doug: Oh, my mom cooks a lot of great food.

E. Kim: I really like those earrings over there.

Sales clerk: _____ ones, the silver ones or the gold ones?

F. Martin: Those desserts look really good!

Maureen: Let's get one.

Martin: _____ one should

　　　　　　1
we get?

Maureen: Let's get the chocolate cake and
the pie, and we can share them.

Waiter: That's a very good choice.

_____ would you

　　　　2
like to drink?

G. Scott: Let's meet at the coffee shop.

Frank: _____ one?

　　　　　1

Scott: The one next to the campus bookstore.

Frank: Okay, _____ time?

　　　　　　　2

Scott: About 7:00.

H. Principal: I need to talk to you about one of your students.

Teacher: _____ one?

　　　　　1

Principal: The young man in the corner over there.

Teacher: Why? _____ happened?

　　　　　　　2

12 Practice

Write answers to the questions.

1. Which day of the week is your favorite?

   _____ .

2. What's your favorite color?

   _____ .

3. Which hand do you write with?

   _____ .

4. Which season is your favorite?

   _____ .

5. Which parent are you closer to?

   _____ .

6. What languages do you speak?

   _____ .

7e Questions with *How*

Student Book p. 171

13 Practice

Complete the sentences with *how, how long, how many, how far, how much*, or *how often*.

A. Jarod and his family have just moved into a new house, and Jarod is talking to his

new neighbor.

New neighbor: _____ did you live in your old house?
                        1

Jarod: We were there about ten years, but it was too small and a little far

from my job. We needed more room because we have dogs.

New neighbor: _____ dogs do you have?
                        2

Jarod: We have three.

New neighbor: Where do you work?

Jarod: I work at Westco.

New neighbor:	Really, _____ is it?
	<div align="center">3</div>
Jarod:	Not far. I can ride my bike to work.
New neighbor:	_____ about your wife? Does she work?
	<div align="center">4</div>
Jarod:	Yes, she's a musician. She plays piano at some of the local jazz clubs.
New neighbor:	_____ does she play?
	<div align="center">5</div>
Jarod:	She usually plays three times a week.

B. Friends are lost.

Wendy:	_____ is it?
	1
Delores:	I'm not sure.
Wendy:	_____ do we get there?
	2
Delores:	I don't know. I think we're lost.
Wendy:	_____ gas do we have?
	3
Delores:	We have enough.
Wendy:	Let's ask that woman over there.
Delores:	Okay, excuse me. _____ miles is it to the beach?
	4
Woman:	You're close. Just turn around and go back. Take a right at the light.

C.

Sheila:	What a wonderful costume! _____ did you make it?
	1
Diana:	Thanks. I found the directions on the Internet. It was easy.
Sheila:	Was the material expensive? Can I ask you _____ it cost?
	2
Diana:	It was pretty cheap.

14 Practice

Complete the questions. Note that some questions with *how* are considered impolite.

1. Tim: _____ old are you?

Victoria: That's none of your business!

2. Beth: _____ do you weigh?

Janice: That's a rude question!

3. Jong: _____ money do you make?

Fran: I can't believe you're asking me that. Didn't your parents teach you

that that's a rude question?

15 Practice

Take a trivia quiz! Match the questions with the answers.

_____ 1. Which country eats the most chocolate every year?

_____ 2. What's the capital of Egypt?

_____ 3. How many time zones are there in the world?

_____ 4. What's the chemical symbol for water?

_____ 5. Who invented the microscope?

_____ 6. What country consumes the most tea?

_____ 7. What country produces the most gold?

a. Zacharias Janssen

b. H_2O

c. Switzerland—22 pounds/year/person

d. India

e. South Africa

f. 24

g. Cairo

16 Practice

Complete the silly jokes. Read the first part of each joke. It asks a question. Try to answer it in a funny way. Your teacher has possible answers.

1. Three frogs are sitting on a lily pad. One decides to jump. How many are left?

   _____.

2. What animal can jump higher than a house?

   _____.

3. Why do birds fly south for the winter?

   _____.

4. What time is it when an elephant sits on your fence?

   _____.

5. Where does Friday come before Thursday?

   _____.

6. How many elephants can fit in your car?

   _____.

7f Tag Questions

Student Book p. 177

17 Practice

Write C next to the sentence if the tag question is correct. Write I if the tag question is incorrect.

_____ 1. He's the boss, isn't it?

_____ 2. Laura and Mike weren't there, were they?

_____ 3. It's cold today, isn't it?

_____ 4. You're from Mexico, are you?

_____ 5. I'm included, aren't I?

_____ 6. Kyle hasn't left, didn't he?

_____ 7. They'll be there, will they?

_____ 8. Sam didn't sleep well, did he?

_____ 9. It wasn't what you expected, wasn't it?

_____ 10. Catlin doesn't understand, does she?

18 Practice

Complete the sentences with the correct tag question.

1. Melissa is in a bad mood, _____?

2. Kate doesn't like spinach, _____?

3. I'm coming too, _____?

4. We don't have time for coffee, _____?

5. It's hot today, _____?

6. This test isn't hard, _____?

7. You've been to Chicago, _____?

8. They need to study more, _____?

9. Alice wears glasses, _____?

10. Mr. Daniels didn't get the message, _____?

11. We should go now, _____?

12. You haven't eaten yet, _____?

13. Our parents will meet us at the hotel, _____?

14. Tag questions are easy, _____?

15. We're finished, _____?

19 Practice

Complete the conversations with the correct tag questions and short answers.

A. Rose: You're not listening, _____?
    1

   Tina: I don't have a choice, _____?
    2

   Rose: You don't care, _____?
    3

   Tina: Yes, _____. But you're always right, _____?
    4   5

B. Adam: You're going, _____?
    1

   Patricia: No, _____.
    2

   Adam: Why?

   Patricia: I took some medicine.

   Adam: You're not sick, _____?
    3

   Patricia: Yes, _____. A little.
    4

20 Practice

Emile is studying for a science test. His older brother Walter is helping him. Complete the conversation with the correct tag questions and short answers.

Emile: Elephants can swim, _____?
    1

Walter: Yes, _____.
    2

Emile: Penguins don't fly, _____?
    3

Walter: No, _____.
    4

Emile: The sun is 93 million miles away, _____?
    5

Walter: Yes, _____.
    6

Emile: The longest river in the world is the Amazon,

_____?
    7

Walter:	No, _____. The Nile is the longest river.
	8
Emile:	Bombay is in Pakistan, _____?
	9
Walter:	No, _____. It's in India.
	10
Emile:	Galileo was Italian, _____?
	11
Walter:	Yes, _____.
	12
Emile:	He invented the microscope, _____?
	13
Walter:	No, _____. That was Zacharias Janssen.
	14
Emile:	Dogs can't see in color, _____?
	15
Walter:	No, _____.
	16

7g Phrasal Verbs

Student Book p. 180

[21] Practice

Read the sentences. Write *T* next to the sentence if the phrasal verb is transitive. Write *I* if the phrasal verb is intransitive.

_____ **1.** They haven't gotten up yet.

_____ **2.** I'll call him back later.

_____ **3.** Mom came across my old high school photos in the attic.

_____ **4.** I hope the car doesn't break down.

_____ **5.** Please don't wake up the baby.

_____ **6.** I always stay up late working.

_____ **7.** We'll go over phrasal verbs one more time before the test.

_____ **8.** I ran into my ex-boyfriend at the movies.

_____ **9.** Could you look after my dog this weekend?

_____ **10.** They got back late last night.

Intransitive Phrasal Verbs

Student Book p. 181

22 Practice

Write *C* next to the sentence if the phrasal verb is correct. Write *I* if the phrasal verb is incorrect.

_____ **1.** Let's sit down them.

_____ **2.** The people stood up when the judge entered the courtroom.

_____ **3.** Xavier has a headache. He's lying down.

_____ **4.** The Feins set out it late yesterday morning.

_____ **5.** Smitty's motorcycle broke down in front of the bank.

_____ **6.** Vivian wants to stay up to watch the eclipse of the moon.

_____ **7.** We got up them at 6:00.

_____ **8.** When did you get back it?

23 Practice

Circle the correct phrasal verb.

1. If you don't feel well, (stand up / lie down).

2. Another way to say *return* is (go back / get up).

3. My back hurts. I need to (set out / stand up).

4. Sophia wants to go to the play, but it doesn't start until 10:00. She's going to (stay up / sit down) late.

5. My grandfather (gets up / breaks down) at 4:30 in the morning.

24 Practice

Write answers to the following questions.

1. On the bus, do you prefer to stand up or sit down? _____.

Why? _____.

2. Do you like to stay up late or get up early? _____.

Why? _____.

3. When do you prefer to set out on vacation, in the early morning or later in the day?

_____. Why? _____.

7i Transitive Phrasal Verbs: Separable

Student Book p. 183

25 Practice

Circle the correct phrasal verb. Then rewrite the sentences, changing the position of the objects.

1. Madelyn, please (pick up / look up) your clothes.

2. If you don't want those old papers, (throw them away / wake them up).

3. Jessica (turned on / called back) her MP3 player.

4. Rob needs to (look up / fill out) the application.

5. Rick, you said you were on a diet. (Put down / Put off) the ice cream cone, and move slowly away from the table.

1. _Madelyn, please pick your clothes up_____.

2. _____.

3. _____.

4. _____.

5. _____.

26 Practice

Complete the sentences with phrasal verbs from the list and the objects in parentheses.

call back	pick up	throw out	wake up
look up	put off	turn on	write down

Ms. Jarvis is meeting Mr. Harris, a very important client, today. She's discussing plans for the meeting with her assistant, David Harn.

Ms. Jarvis: David, please (the schedule) _____ for me.
                                                              1

David: Sure.

Ms. Jarvis: Could you please (my other appointments) _____
                                                                            2

until next week? I'm going to be very busy today. I'd like to take a

nap, so please (me) _____ at 1:30. Who is
                                         3

(Mr. Harris) _____ at the airport?
                         4

David: We sent a limousine.

Ms. Jarvis: Good. Could you please (the numbers) _____
                                                                  5

of some of the other people in his office? I may need to call them later.

David: Of course. By the way, you got a call from Richmond Brothers.

Ms. Jarvis: I'll (them) _____ tomorrow. The conference room
                                    6
                is very warm, and it's not cleaned up.

David: I'll (the air conditioning) _____ and
                                                    7
                (any trash) _____ that's in the room.
                                  8

Ms. Jarvis: Thanks, David.

27 | Practice

Write as many things as you can for each category.

1. Things that you throw out

   a. _____

   b. _____

   c. _____

2. Things you put off

   a. _____

   b. _____

   c. _____

3. Things you pick up

   a. _____

   b. _____

   c. _____

4. Things you look up

   a. _____

   b. _____

   c. _____

5. Things you fill out

   a. _____

   b. _____

   c. _____

6. Things you turn on

a. _____

b. _____

c. _____

7j ◆ Transitive Phrasal Verbs: Inseparable

Student Book p. 186

28 Practice

Circle the correct phrasal verb.

1. Joe had a terrible cold, but he (got over / came across) it.

2. Theresa (got out / ran into) her English teacher at the theater.

3. Everyone had to (get off / get into) the bus and wait for another one.

4. She's (going over / looking after) the recipe one more time before we start baking.

5. A nanny is someone who (looks after / looks into) children.

6. I was late because I (got on / got over) the wrong bus.

7. Employee: My check was wrong.

   Boss: I'll (run into / look into) it.

8. George was cleaning out his backpack and (got into / came across) an old letter

   from 2003.

29 Practice

Write *C* next to the sentence if the phrasal verb is used correctly. Write *I* if the phrasal verb is used incorrectly. Some phrasal verbs are separable and some are inseparable.

_____ **1.** Nurses look the patients after.

_____ **2.** She put it off until next week.

_____ **3.** I didn't pick it up. It was dirty.

_____ **4.** My little sister ran the neighbors into at the grocery store.

_____ **5.** We looked into it.

_____ **6.** Karl turned it off before he went to bed.

A **Choose the best answer, A, B, C, or D, to complete the sentence. Mark your answer by darkening the oval with the same letter.**

1. Jan: _____ 's your homework?
   Andreas: On the desk.

   A. Who   Ⓐ Ⓑ Ⓒ Ⓓ
   B. Where
   C. What
   D. When

2. _____ money does he have?

   A. How many   Ⓐ Ⓑ Ⓒ Ⓓ
   B. How about
   C. How much
   D. How

3. Mom's really tired. She's going to _____.

   A. lie down   Ⓐ Ⓑ Ⓒ Ⓓ
   B. get up
   C. go over
   D. stand up

4. He's a teacher, _____?

   A. he isn't   Ⓐ Ⓑ Ⓒ Ⓓ
   B. isn't he
   C. he is
   D. he's

5. _____ were you talking to?

   A. Where   Ⓐ Ⓑ Ⓒ Ⓓ
   B. What
   C. When
   D. Who

6. Have your parents retired yet? _____

   A. Yes, they are.   Ⓐ Ⓑ Ⓒ Ⓓ
   B. No, they didn't.
   C. Yes, they did.
   D. Yes, they have.

7. She doesn't smoke, _____?

   A. does she   Ⓐ Ⓑ Ⓒ Ⓓ
   B. doesn't she
   C. she doesn't
   D. she does

8. The milk is really old. _____

   A. Throw out it.   Ⓐ Ⓑ Ⓒ Ⓓ
   B. Put it on.
   C. Throw it out.
   D. Put it off.

9. _____ one did you pick?

   A. What   Ⓐ Ⓑ Ⓒ Ⓓ
   B. Which
   C. How
   D. Where

10. Your brother can drive, _____?

    A. can he   Ⓐ Ⓑ Ⓒ Ⓓ
    B. he can
    C. he can't
    D. can't he

B **Find the underlined word or phrase, A, B, C, or D, that is incorrect. Mark your answer by darkening the oval with the same letter.**

1. You <u>didn't</u> <u>look</u> up <u>it</u>, did <u>you</u>?
   A   B   C   D

   Ⓐ Ⓑ Ⓒ Ⓓ

2. <u>Who</u> happened to <u>the store</u> <u>on</u>
   A   B   C

   <u>the corner</u>?
   D

   Ⓐ Ⓑ Ⓒ Ⓓ

3. <u>She'll</u> <u>met</u> <u>us</u> there, <u>won't</u> <u>she</u>?
   A   B   B   C   D

   Ⓐ Ⓑ Ⓒ Ⓓ

4. <u>The artist</u> <u>paint</u> landscape <u>paintings</u>,
   A   B   C

   didn't <u>he</u>?
          D

   Ⓐ Ⓑ Ⓒ Ⓓ

5. We <u>didn't</u> <u>wake up</u> <u>it</u> early this morning,
   A   B   C

   <u>did we</u>?
   D

   Ⓐ Ⓑ Ⓒ Ⓓ

6. <u>Our class</u> <u>went over</u> the questions,
   A   B

   <u>didn't</u> <u>I</u>?
   C   D

   Ⓐ Ⓑ Ⓒ Ⓓ

7. <u>Who</u> is the teacher <u>going to</u> <u>hand back</u>
   A   B   C

   <u>the tests</u>?
   D

   Ⓐ Ⓑ Ⓒ Ⓓ

8. <u>How much</u> times <u>did</u> <u>we</u> <u>talk</u> about this?
   A   B   C   D

   Ⓐ Ⓑ Ⓒ Ⓓ

9. <u>When</u> <u>was waiting</u> for Kate <u>after</u> school
   A   B   C

   <u>this afternoon</u>?
   D

   Ⓐ Ⓑ Ⓒ Ⓓ

10. The team <u>has won</u> the championship
              A

    every year <u>for</u> the past <u>five years</u>,
               B   C

    <u>has it</u>?
    D

    Ⓐ Ⓑ Ⓒ Ⓓ